LOOK WIDE

LOOK WIDE

A BOOK FOR SENIOR SCOUTS

Published by
The Boy Scouts Association
25 Buckingham Palace Road
London, S.W.1

First Published – *1956*
Second Edition – *1961*
Reprinted – *1962*

Printed by
KENT PAPER COMPANY LIMITED
LONDON, AND ASHFORD, KENT

CONTENTS

PAGE

Prologue

By the Chief Scout 7

I. Life and You

1. What's Life to You? by Laurence Stringer ... 11
2. ". . . To do my duty to God . . ." by Wilfred Wade 19
3. Pure in Body and Mind, by The Rev. O. J. Lambert ... ...
4. Physical Fitness, by Altham Turner 39
5. The World You Live In, by V. G. Hines ... 50
6. The Queen's Scout Badge, by George Witchell 60
7. The Senior Scout and his place in the Movement, by Hubert Blore 64
8. The Duke of Edinburgh's Award 71

II. The Open Air

9. Camping and Hiking, by John Sweet ... 79
10. Expeditions with Trike-carts, by J. A. Blake ... 90
11. Camping Abroad, by C. T. H. Burton ... 101
12. Rock Climbing and Mountaineering, by Lt.-Cmdr. Showell Styles 112
13. Caving, by A. L. Butcher 122
14. The World of Nature, by Michael Blackmore 134

III. The Critical Attitude

15. Reading, by Rex Hazlewood   145
16. The Arts (Music, Painting, Architecture), by
    Peter Traxton   151
17. Films and the Theatre, by Jack Singleton   ...   163
18. Acting and Play Producing, by Ralph Reader   173
19. Social Occasions, by Olive Thurman   179

Appendix

Sixty Suggested Activities   191

LOOK WIDER!

First you had "The Senior Scout Handbook" and from this came "Look Wide". Now you have this revised, enlarged and right up to date copy of a book which has been of interest and assistance to many Senior Scouts.

This new edition is the natural continuation of the original edition. It has grown in stature just as you have grown year by year. I believe the title might well have been changed to "Look Wider" — because this is in fact just what this book has done.

While you read through these pages and when you put into practice

Some of the many ideas which they contain remember that it is YOUR efforts, YOUR ENTHUSIASM and YOUR example which will make or break the ideas which you have been given.

Charles Maclean

20th Sept 1960.

Part 1

LIFE AND YOU

Chapter 1

WHAT'S LIFE TO YOU?

THE title of this chapter poses a question, a question which everyone should be prepared to answer and yet about which comparatively few ever really concern themselves. After all, what does it really matter provided you get the best out of life and enjoy every moment of your existence to the full, let us "eat, drink and be merry, for tomorrow we die." Some would go even further and say that as they did not ask to come into the world they are fully entitled, now that they are here, to take as much out of life as they can and that their responsibilities begin and end there.

"Eat, drink and be merry, for tomorrow we die."

Well, what do you think about it —you who are young and who are standing before a gateway which leads to so many new and exciting experiences? I hope that you may have some pretty definite answers, but I shall try during the course of this chapter to give you a few ideas which may help to clarify your views and, possibly, assist you by making a few suggestions for your consideration.

Life, we are told, is what you make it. As a generalisation that is a fairly accurate statement and, therefore, the subject with which we are dealing is one of considerable importance.

I think we can assume that every boy and young man wishes to make a success of life. From very early days we are taught to put our best efforts into whatever we do, be it work or play. The young athlete tries to improve upon his time over a certain distance, the footballer continually practises his ball technique and control, the cricketer endeavours to further his ability as batsman or bowler, the student pursues his studies in order that he may succeed with his examinations, and so we might go on. And so it is with life. There are, of course, many people in the world who do not agree with this and who adopt the point of view that I mentioned at the commencement of this chapter—that they have every right to take as much as they can and give nothing in return. It is a poor attitude and one which must inevitably lead to bankruptcy in some way or another.

When God gave us life I am sure that He gave it to us for a purpose. Our coming here was no accident; it was part of God's plan. Although God is the Author of the Plan of Life, He has given us a large measure of freedom of choice as to how we carry out our part of it. This freedom allows us to work out our own lives as best we may, but, having exercised this freedom, we must not lose sight of the fact that God is ready to help us on our journey through life if we wish to avail ourselves of His divine assistance. It is true to say that, although He will not show us the future, He is prepared to go with us all the way.

Whilst it is not my intention to dwell upon the religious aspect of life, I wish to say quite early on that I am sure that life and God cannot be disassociated—they are very closely joined, and we should realise that He Who created us is always there to assist us.

Shall we then, bearing this in mind, get down to trying to sort out in our own minds what factors and influences in life really have a bearing on our idea of what life means? I would like to put some suggestions before you for your thought and consideration—in some cases leaving you to draw your own conclusions.

In our reading and from personal contacts with people we have had our imagination and admiration fired by the influence and example which they have exerted or are exerting on their fellow-men. What single fact is it that

12

makes them great? I suggest that it is that their lives have displayed a desire to serve their fellow-men. They have devoted themselves to this end without thought of personal gain. One thinks of men like Albert Schweitzer, who, despite his talents and accomplishments which could have brought him wealth and renown, has devoted practically the whole of his life to improving the lot of the native in Central Africa. No ordinary human being can fail to be moved by such a display of unselfish service. A desire to assist those less fortunate than themselves is surely an admirable attribute which can be possessed by us all. That well-known organisation, Toc H, sums all this up by saying that "service is the rent we pay for our room on earth." I commend it to you.

The fact is that no matter how difficult things are, or how hard pressed you and I may be, there is always someone less fortunate who needs our help, and in rendering such assistance we not only serve our brothers, but, by the same act, aid ourselves by turning our own thoughts away from our personal worries and problems. In so doing, we are surely helping to develop another great quality—that of unselfishness. The world in which we are living today needs, possibly more than ever before, young men and, indeed, people of all ages who are prepared to serve others. The opportunities are unlimited because there are so many who need help in some way or other and comparatively few who are prepared to devote themselves unselfishly to something which provides no material reward. Is there a field in which you and I might render service? I suggest that if we are sufficiently keen to seek, there are many and life would become that much richer for us because we are serving others—and service provides its own reward in the great satisfaction that is derived out of having made somebody's lot in life less difficult, some unfortunate or unhappy man or woman happier. What a wonderful privilege! What a challenge! What an opportunity!

I have written at some length upon this matter because I feel it is so vital to real happiness and it is beyond

13

dispute that there is a very close relationship between service and unselfishness. Some time ago I heard a true story which links up the next point which I wish to make regarding kindness and thought for others. It concerns a boy of twelve who broke his back while riding. The doctor couldn't do anything for him. All that they could do was to deaden the pain. One day when they had failed, after he had had a particularly bad spasm, he said to his mother, "Wasn't it jolly lucky that the pony wasn't hurt —only me!" I shall never forget the impact that that story had upon myself, and those two words "only me" at the end. That young boy died a few days later, but his example shines like a blazing beacon in a world which so desperately needs such a disregard for self and kindly thought for others—and only twelve years old! This, surely, is the real way of life.

Let us move on. We hear a great deal today about independence and individal freedom of one kind or another. Some people tend to be so selfish and self-centred that they don't care about the rights of others as long as they enjoy themselves and, in so doing, they trample over those who are weaker, less privileged. They say, "Why worry about other people's opinions or ways of life? If they provide an obstacle to my happiness, then I shall just

"Their opinions are the only ones worth consideration."

push them aside." There are others, too, who think that their opinions are the only ones worthy of consideration. They have no time to listen to what others have to say, even though, by listening, they might be hearing the voice of experience and reason. It was Mark Twain who is reported to have once said, "When I was fourteen I thought my father was a very stupid man, but when I was twenty-one I was surprised to see how much he had learned in such a short time." Might I make a plea for a tolerant outlook? Tolerance is the generosity that concedes to others the rights to their opinions and peculiarities. It is the bigness that enables us to let people be happy in their way, not in ours. It is the most lovable quality any human being can possess. How much happier life would be for us all if we really tried to consider the other fellow's point of view and accorded to him the right to his own opinions, even if we don't agree with them! We might, too, do well to remember those words of Mark Twain.

Turning to the other side of the picture we find that there are some who are so easily swayed and influenced by people that they fail to have any opinions of their own, or, if they possess them, are weak enough to surrender them on the slightest pretext. Whilst it is right to listen to others, we must maintain our own views and standards if those presented by others are not, in our opinion, as good as our own. The fellow who swims with the tide on all occasions is not worth much, especially if it means sacrificing his principles to do so. Courage in the face of temptation and difficulty from whatever source it may come, will surely help to keep up the moral and spiritual standards of the world in which we are living. I suggest that the fellow who fights back in the face of adversity or even defeat, be it in sport or life, who never surrenders the dignity of his soul for material reward, will be the chap who ultimately derives the greatest triumph and satisfaction out of living. Am I right? Or is what I have written an exaggeration? Well, think about it for a moment. Who are the people for whom you have the greatest admiration? Those who have performed feats and for whom everything has been comparatively easy, or those who have fought against tremendous odds, who have not always triumphed but have left their mark on life? Scott of the Antarctic, Mallory, Orde Wingate, Franklin Roosevelt are but a few, and there are many others. They climbed, they fought, they planned and, in so doing, showed to their fellow-men the indomitable spirit of man. Endeavour was their theme and they proved over and over again that man's greatest glory is not in never failing, but in rising every time he falls. This is the

15

message that they have left for those of us who are trying to find out what life should mean.

Now I want to place another matter before you. It concerns the art of "being natural." By this I mean being our own selves on all occasions. I don't doubt that we have met the person who is continually trying to impress others with his or her own importance.

An air of artificiality surrounds them, so much so that one is sorely tempted to tell them to "come off it"—to come "down to earth." How foolish this attitude is, for it is not long before the discerning person sees through the veneer and, let us be frank, the hypocrisy that is theirs. My experience of life has shown me that the art of being one's self is one of the finest qualities that can be possessed. After all, what does it really matter when compared with the most worthwhile things of life what people think about us, providing we are honestly trying to live a good life? This doesn't mean that we have no consideration for the opinions of others. Of course, we like to be thought well of and even to be popular members of the community—but popularity is all right until one goes in search of it. Yes, let us aim at being ourselves.

"An air of artificiality surrounds them."

A short time ago I heard some young fellows discussing a church service which they had just attended. One of the fellows said this: "I quite enjoyed the service, the hymns were jolly good, the anthem sounded pleasant and the preacher wasn't at all bad, and, incidentally, I felt quite 'religious' during the service." All very fine, you may say, but I suggest to you that, commendable though these observations appeared to be, the chap making them had got his priorities all wrong. Should it not have been this way round? "I felt quite 'religious' during the service and, incidentally, the hymns, anthem and preacher were good."

16

We are inclined to get things out of perspective at times and, like the young man just mentioned, get the affairs of life in incorrect order of importance. There is, for instance, a tendency for some people who are very keen on fostering good friendly relationships to forget that friendship begins in one's own home and country. I have even come across Scouts who are wildly enthusiastic about being friendly with every foreign Scout they meet, and yet the Troop of which they are a member is always at loggerheads with the one which has its headquarters in the next street. See what I mean? The matter can be carried further. What, after all, are the really important things in life—wealth, position, dress, the manner of one's speech, or does it matter more if we are honest, straightforward, unselfish, kindly disposed to others and ready to help those who are in need? The answer might appear to be obvious, but in our living do you and I always find that answer?

You who have come so far through this chapter may be thinking that, if all I have written and if there is any merit in the suggestions that I have put before you, the business of living must be a very serious affair. I think it is. Every one of us has a great responsibility to the world in which we live. Having established this point, I wish to conclude on a lighter note.

Life is a great adventure, and by that I mean that almost every moment should provide you with the opportunity of finding out something new and of enjoying fresh experiences. It is not for us all to climb Everest, but the same spirit that urged Brigadier Sir John Hunt and his team on to final victory is there for us in our various and varied assaults on life. We must venture forth into the unknown as they did. The Everest team did not know all the problems that they might meet on

"It is not for all of us to climb Everest."

17

the way to their objective, but in a spirit of courage and endeavour they tackled them as they came along—and triumphed. This is what the leader said when it was all over:—

"Was it worth while? For us who took part in the venture, it was so beyond doubt. We have shared a high endeavour; we have witnessed scenes of beauty and grandeur; we have built up a lasting comradeship among ourselves and we have seen the fruits of that comradeship ripen into achievement. We shall not forget those moments of great living upon that mountain.

And what of others? Was it worth while for them, too? I believe it may have been, if it is accepted that there is a need for adventure in the world we live in, and provided, too, that it is realised that adventure can be found in many spheres, not merely upon a mountain, and not necessarily physical. Ultimately, the justification for climbing Everest, if any justification is needed, will lie in the seeking of their 'Everests' by others, stimulated by this event as we were inspired by others before us. There are many opportunities for adventure, whether they be sought among the hills, in the air, upon the sea, in the bowels of the earth, or upon the ocean bed, and there is always the moon to reach. There is no height, no depth, that the spirit of man, guided by a higher Spirit, cannot attain."

"There is always the moon to reach."

Go forward, seeking your "Everests" and I hope that on your journey you, too, will witness scenes of beauty and grandeur, that you will find lasting comradeships and that you may see your efforts ripen into achievement.

What will be the final verdict on your life? Will it be this?—that the world is a better place because you have lived in it. God grant that it may be so for each one of us.

Chapter 2

"..... TO DO MY DUTY TO GOD....."

By The Rev. Wilfred Wade

(Chairman of the Cornwall District of the Methodist Church)

SO far as the ordinary man is concerned, life today seems well under control. Less than three hundred years ago, Isaac Watts was writing:

> *"Dangers stand thick through all the ground*
> *To push us to the tomb;*
> *And fierce diseases wait around*
> *To hurry mortals home."*

What a smile would go round the Scouts' Own if we were asked to sing that now! No, today things give the impression of being well in hand. A baby, for example, is in the care of the local clinic even before it is born; there are opportunities of education beyond anything our grandparents dreamed of; there's the Ministry of Labour to help one find a job—and a Trade Union to prevent one losing it; insurance companies almost queue for the privilege of carrying the risk of our home being burgled; and the Odeon is only five minutes' walk away!

"A baby is in the care of the local clinic."

In such a world God seems unnecessary.

True, the ordinary man doesn't call himself an Atheist—he just acts like one!

The Communist, of course, goes further. He argues

that events are dominated by historical necessity; that God was invented by the propertied-classes to keep the unprivileged in their place; that the only driving force in the world is economic interest; and that Man is merely the cleverest of the animals.

With this as the background of our everyday life, it isn't surprising that a lot of fellows, as they reach Senior Scout and Rover age, begin to wonder whether the First Promise has any modern relevance.

Let's think, then, about our belief in God.

I might begin by writing of Him as One with Whom I am personally acquainted. But unless you stand in the same personal relationship, that soon becomes boring. (I remember how, when I left school, and started work in a Manchester laboratory, one of my workmates was always talking about his Aunt Rose. I'd never met her, and I grew tired of hearing of her! I couldn't have cared less! I don't want that to happen at this point.) So let's make a different start—let's begin on common ground— let's look at ourselves and our surroundings, and ask Who created us and them?

Ourselves. Here we are, fabricated upon a backbone; given movement by hundreds of hinges and muscles; kept fresh and alert by a process of inflation that goes on about eighteen times a minute, twenty-four hours a day, waking and sleeping, as long as we live; able to see and hear;

"Capable of unspeakable cruelty."

able to communicate with our fellows; so co-ordinated that we're possessed of a thousand skills (able to dismantle a bike and to thread a needle, able to swerve at speed on the rugby field and to read and play a Chopin Prelude); gladdened (or shamed!) by memory; stirred by deep emotions; capable of unshakable loyalty—but also capable of unspeakable cruelty; and all of us moving inexorably to the day when we shall die. Who gave us a life of such quality, and provides the conditions for its survival? *We* didn't!

Again, look at our surroundings.

Think of the sheer mass of the world we inhabit.

Eight thousand miles through; yet possessed of terrifying motion! Spinning on its axis at a thousand miles an hour; simultaneously tearing round its mighty orbit of the sun at eighteen and a half miles a second—and with it all, swaying so gently as to produce the seasons in the northern and southern hemispheres!

Think of the world's variety—rock and metal; sea and vegetation; insect and elephant; mobile and stationary; soft and hard; arctic and tropical—yet everything in it based upon the various combinations of ninety-two chemical elements! Indeed, if the scientists are right, everything ultimately a variant of the one energy!

Who is responsible for that? *We* aren't!

Nor does it end there.

"Insect and elephant."

Think beyond the Earth of the Universe around it! Imagine the speed of the fastest jets in service with the R.A.F. Light travels just about a million times faster than that! And if we could travel *at the speed of light* it would still take us four and a quarter *years* to reach the nearest star: and over a million years to reach the farthest (known) star!

It may be possible to go through a routine day, with all its comfortable twentieth-century safeguards, never giving a thought to God—yet as soon as we face Reality, either in ourselves or our surroundings, Reason itself compels us to believe in Him! These things didn't just happen! If Chance accounts for them, then they are quite unpredictable, and Science itself becomes impossible. As it is, they are orderly, dependable, balanced. And because that is so, Agriculture, Medicine, Engineering, Marriage become reasonable.

Theology offers a good many other reasons for believing in God (and if you wanted to pursue them, your chaplain

21

would gladly lend you books, etc.). Personally, I find the argument I've outlined more than persuasive.

Yet, even when we conclude that God is, the fundamental question remains, "Can we know Him?"

Clearly, if the answer is "Yes," it is only because He chooses to be known. One capable of creating and sustaining so vast a Universe would be beyond His creatures' comprehension unless He had Himself decided otherwise.

Religious thinkers all over the world believe God *has* decided otherwise. He has chosen to reveal Himself.

As a Christian I believe He has done that in the character and achievement of Jesus Christ. At this point some of you may want to hesitate, and to ask "Why particularise? Isn't the revelation in Islam, or Hinduism, or Buddhism just as valid?" For me, the plain answer is "No." I believe that Christianity offers keener insights and higher values than any other faith, and that it deals more honestly and satisfyingly with the awkward and irrational elements in human experience (things like pain, and earthquakes, and evil).

Now at this point I stand where St. Paul did—I believe that the truth of the Christian revelation of God depends on the historicity of Christ's resurrection. "If Christ has not been raised, then our preaching is in vain and your faith is in vain." (1 Cor. 15, v. 14.) The guarantee that what Jesus lived and died for is of God Himself is that Jesus returned from the dead. Without that guarantee He might have been thought just another good but mistaken martyr.

So, even if it appears to be a digression, I'm going to ask you to pause, and to weigh the evidence for the Resurrection in your own mind. It seems to me to bear the closest scrutiny. If we dismiss it as myth, we must dismiss everything else in recorded history. After all, there's quite as much evidence for it as there is for the coming of William the Conqueror! The records begin by making it clear that Jesus *did* die—we're not concerned with a man who merely swooned, and who in the cold of a rock sepulchre later revived. He died. But on the third

22

day His grave was found to be empty. Some have tried
to suggest that in the half-light of that first Easter morning the disciples went to the *wrong* tomb, and finding it
empty jumped to the false conclusion that He had risen.
But there were repeated visits to the grave that day;
would the same mistake be made again and again? And
if it were, why didn't the authorities simply produce the
Body still under guard, and so make laughing-stocks of
the disciples? No, He died, but on the third day His
grave was empty. And that to the complete surprise of
His followers! These weren't men who were credulous,
half-persuaded before anything happened! Read the
accounts for yourself—here were level-headed young men
who at first refused to believe the plain facts, and needed
repeated and varied evidence before they would accept the
frightening truth. In the end they were convinced—convinced not only because His grave was empty, but because
they'd encountered Him in person! That made new men
of them! (Again, the evidence is overwhelming.) Instead
of being muddle-headed, quarrelsome cowards, they became wise, steady, united, courageous leaders—ready to
die (as most of them did die) rather than abandon their
conviction that Jesus had risen from the dead. And that
conviction they made public, not years afterwards and a
thousand miles away, but at once, and in the very place
where they said it had happened, and where it could be
disproved *if it were not true.*

I come back, then, to the point I was making earlier—
the Christian revelation of what God is like is authenti-
cated by the Resurrection of the Lord Jesus.

Notice some of the things He said.

For example, "All things have been delivered to me by
my Father; and no one knows the Son except the Father,
and no one knows the Father except the Son *and any one
to whom* the Son chooses to reveal Him." (Matthew 11,
v. 27.) Again, "I am the way, and the truth, and the life;
no one comes to the Father, but by me." (John 14, v. 6.)
What I want you to observe is that Jesus claimed to reveal
God. Similarly, He claimed to know Life's answer's; for

example, "Everyone who comes to me and hears my words and does them, I will show you what he is like; he is like a man building a house, who dug deep, and laid the foundation on rock . . . but he who hears and does not do them is like a man who built a house on the ground without a foundation; against which the stream broke, and immediately it fell, and the ruin of that house was great." (Luke 6, vv. 47-49.)

All that sounds vigorous enough. But see how it works out in practice.

"The word became flesh and dwelt among us." Here's life with all its perplexities and disappointments—and it's as though God had taken a job in the factory Himself! If you want to know what God is like, at the level where it matters most, you look into the Gospels, not into the sky! He's most vivid in the character of Jesus; not in the mathematics of the astronomer! He sees the inequalities of life: He doesn't *order* a re-distribution: instead, by His own act, God teaches men to care, and to share! He sees the coarseness and cruelty of which we are capable; He doesn't establish a Ministry of Re-education: instead, He *befriends* the cruel and the coarse, the publicans and sinners! When men decide they can't bear His nearness, He doesn't lose patience. They crucify Him, but the Cross doesn't so much show what we are like as what He is like.

"A perfunctory atten-dance at church parade."

All this means we shall be living the sanest kind of life if we take Jesus seriously. "Duty to God" isn't a perfunctory attendance at church parade; it's the acknowledgment of One Who has a total claim upon our loyalty and our time. Our promise isn't kept by occasional church-going; it involves study of the teaching and aims of the Lord Jesus as they're recorded in the Gospels; it involves allegiance to the world-wide comradeship He established (His Church); it means recognising that we are answerable to Him for the way we do our job, for our friendships, for our use of money, and time—yes, and of our own bodies and minds.

All this would be rather overwhelming were it not for one fact—He Who claims our duty offers His own friendship! We may begin the religious life by acknowledging a claim; we don't pursue it far without discovering it's brought us into a relationship—more satisfying and vital than anything else life holds. I hope you won't rest contented until you're in that relationship—for keeps.

Chapter 3

PURE IN BODY AND MIND

To live the life of nature is to think the thoughts of nature; to live the life of the spirit is to think the thoughts of the spirit; and natural wisdom brings only death, whereas the wisdom of the spirit brings life and peace.

St. Paul's Epistle to the Romans, viii, 5 and 6.

EVERYONE consists of body and of soul. My body has arms and legs, heart, lungs, etc.; it has flesh and blood, nerves and senses. My soul, or mind, is what I think with; my mind is what remembers and chooses. Body and mind are very different from one another— bodies are some colour or other: red, yellow, black, or the sort of pale pink that ours are, and which we flatter ourselves by calling "white": bodies weigh so many pounds and are so many feet tall. But you cannot cut off a yard of memory, or weigh out an ounce of choice; and, except in a poetical way of talking, you cannot speak of a "black" thought, or being in a "blue" mood. Body and soul, in short, consist of matter, and of spirit; yet they work in union with one another and make me into a human "person": directly my soul leaves my body, my body is a "corpse," and begins to fall to pieces and soon enough is dust. But my soul does not die. If I want to be a good specimen of a man, I must keep my soul—my thoughts, my memory, my will-power—in good condition; and also, so far as possible, my body. But since it is my soul which makes my body to *be* a body, my mind ought to control my body, and I ought first and foremost to keep my mind in good condition, as I shall say later. But first I will say what my body is meant for.

First, it is meant to keep alive and fit; this is why I

have the instinct to eat. But too much food, or wrong sorts of food, make me sick; then my mind must *control* my instinct and tell me to stop eating if I have had enough, or not to eat what gives me indigestion even if I like it. Then in comes my will, and *wills* to do what my common sense tells me I ought to do. I have, too, the instinct to protect myself—to hit out if someone hits me, or even if he looks as if he meant to: I automatically blink if

"Stop eating when I've had enough."

a fly seems to be going to fly into my eye. Then my mind tells me that I must be able to keep my temper in control and not lose it the moment someone says what

"Keep my temper under control."

I don't like. It also teaches me not to be a coward. I am sure you see how important the mind is. Anyone can hit out blindly; but only with the help of the mind can I learn to *box properly*. Mind and body must work together, mind controlling body.

Another instinct is the one which little by little leads up to a man wanting to marry a woman. It is called the "sex-instinct." "Sex" is a word derived from the Latin *sec-o*, I cut; because human nature is, as it were, cut into two halves, men and women, and normally neither half is complete without the other. They are, in fact, *meant* to be joined together by what is called "marriage," and to be husband and wife, and the parents of children. How does this happen? A boy has in front of him a small tube through which he makes water: the proper name for this is *penis*. Under it is a small bag of skin containing two "balls," for which the proper name is *testicle*. These are extremely sensitive

27

and hurt terribly if they are injured. As a boy grows older, his body should get larger and tougher; his voice "breaks" and gets deeper; more hair grows upon him; he may find that his penis from time to time becomes large and stiff— "erect," as they say—and, most important of all, his testicles begin to make a sort of fluid which is stored up in his body, and periodically this fluid is emptied out of the penis, usually at night, and perhaps accompanied by queer dreams. This natural event should worry no boy, rather, he should take it as a good sign, showing him that he is now a healthy man. This fluid is different from anything else in him. Why? Because, for instance, his spittle, or ear-wax, are dead, and can be got rid of and no harm done. But this fluid, called *seed*, or in Latin *semen*, is full of millions of tiny invisible living creatures which are not only alive, but are meant to *give life*. How do they do that?

A man is not made in the same way as a woman as to "sex." Instead of a "penis," she has a kind of tube leading into a bag called the "womb." If the penis is pushed into this tube, the "semen" will come out and after a while one of its tiny living creatures (it is called by the long name "spermatozoon," which in practice means just "living seed") meets with something else in the woman—tiny too—called "ovum" or "egg." The semen "fertilises" this, and the ovum fixes itself to the side of the womb, and the life of the woman nourishes it, and after nine months it has become a full-grown infant, and is driven out through the tube I mentioned. It is still fastened to the mother by a sort of cord of skin which has to be cut. (Your navel is where this cord was fastened to *you*.) Then the child is completely born. This is the whole account of how a child is "conceived," and "born," except for a very few details of no interest.

That is the proper use to make of this part of your body, but it can also be mis-used, and sometimes it takes a lot of courage to conquer the inclination to mis-use it. These things are being told to you quite simply here because (1) you ought to know about them, for, if you do

28

not, you may make mistakes about yourself, and (2) you are sure to be inquisitive, and to want to know what other boys know, especially if you see them whispering about them as if they were a mysterious secret, and if they laugh at you for *not* knowing, as if you were a baby who mustn't be told such things, then you are sure to try to find out in round-about ways, which are always rather nasty. It is not good to pick up one's information in the gutter. Besides which there cannot possibly be anything wrong about understanding one's own body, and learning how to use it properly. And, incidentally, instinct grows up much quicker than the intelligence or will-power do; we would all like to be men of strong will, but the will needs a great deal of *wise exercise* before it becomes strong, and it cannot get it if you are ignorant.

Now, apart from curiosity, what difficulties are you likely to have? I leave till later what concerns thoughts and talk. You may find that at night (or any other time) you feel uncomfortable and want to rub your penis, and this may produce in it a pleasant sensation, and, if you are old enough, some drops of the "semen" may come out. The name for this act is "masturbation," which means "troubling yourself with your hand." First, be sure that a boy may begin doing this quite innocently; he may find himself doing it without knowing why. Perhaps, if he learns that he should not do it, he may be able to stop quite easily. But he may find it has become a habit and that it means an awful struggle to get out of it—like sillier things such as scratching one's head, biting one's nails, etc.

I will try to say afterwards what it is best to do if that has happened. But the first thing to say is that another name for this solitary act is "self-abuse." That means that one is using one's body the *wrong way*—"self-misuse" might be almost a better expression, because "abuse" has come to mean saying violent and angry things to someone. Anyhow, it is a "mis-use" of the body because the only fully right reason for making the "semen" to flow is for husband to join with wife in giving

29

life to a child. You mustn't think that one or two acts of this sort are going to injure your body: still less, that (as they used to say to frighten boys off it) self-abuse will drive you mad. That is an ignorant untruth, though people still sometimes say it. But it is not good for you (1) because it gives a sort of shock to your nervous system which is too great for a young boy to stand, and if a boy did it *often* he certainly might grow slack and languid and find his back aching, and perhaps feel muddled and lose interest in games and so on, and (2) because it accustoms you to taking pleasure *in yourself*; you might become "self-centred," as they say, and not want to mix freely with other boys; and (3) you might feel you have a sort of guilty secret and be afraid that others guess it, and are staring at you, or that you are somehow "different" from everybody else; and (4) if you want to please God (as I hope you do), you may end by feeling that you *cannot help* doing something that is wrong, and be haunted by this idea and feel that no one can help you, and that God *will* not help you. In short, self-abuse is likely to do much more harm to a boy's mind than to his body.

Anyhow, while you are a boy, this part of your body is meant only for "passing water" (the proper name is "urine") which gets rid of some of the acids that the body is always brewing, just as the other opening, farther back, gets rid of thicker stuff which is the part of food which you do not digest and which does not nourish you, and which would poison you if you kept it very long inside you. It is a very good thing to "pass water" just before going to bed, and to get rid of the rest *regularly,* soon after breakfast if you can. Anyhow, try to make a *habit* of going always at the same time. To be regular in this matter helps also for controlling one's self in the matter we are chiefly talking about. You would be quite astonished what a control the mind can get of our muscles, even of some which most people cannot move at all!

Now I will just explain two other words. If a man performs the act I have mentioned with a woman who is unmarried, and if he is unmarried, that is called "fornication"; if he does it with a married woman not his wife, or if he is married himself, that is "adultery."

*　　*　　*　　*

If you have this instinct, and even if you find it is a difficult one to control, *never think it is a bad one*. It is part of human nature as God made it, and God made nothing that is bad. You will always have it, and probably it will be stronger so long as your body gets stronger, and as long as you have not won experience in controlling it; but it is not *bad*. Angels have no body, so they have not got this instinct: but God did not make you to be an angel, but a *man,* and men have bodies and will until they die.

Next, do not feel frightened of it, as though some day it was bound to make you its victim. Finally, do not feel ashamed of it or imagine that you are the only one to be worried by it. Some boys are luckier than others, and are practically not worried at all. But some day they probably will be; and remember, therefore, that it is quite natural, and *not* bad. Without it I suppose that no one would ever marry or have any children!

Now we must examine this business of "thoughts" more carefully; for, as I said, success depends entirely on self-control, and self-control starts in the mind.

The mind is what makes me human. It, and nothing else, makes me able to judge what is right and wrong. If I pass behind a nervous horse and he kicks me, I do not call him an

"A nervous horse and he kicks me!"

"immoral horse." If I am hungry, or like chocolate, and if I see some, I should simply take and eat it *if I had nothing but instinct*; but if my mind tells me: "No! it belongs to So-and-so; to take it would be stealing"—I

31

stop myself. But I get *some* thoughts that I do not want to have—that is to say, about "sex." I cannot help having these! Talk, pictures, particular persons are always making my mind "think" just as the wind blowing on the sea makes it ripple. How can I get rid of such thoughts? *Not* by "fighting against them." Not by saying: "I will not think of so-and-so." That is like hammering a nail on the head in order to drive it right through and out of the wood. It only drives it farther in. Make—not a frontal attack, but a "flanking movement." Think about *something else*. In daytime, work at some hobby of yours— Scouts ought to have lots. At night—well, think out the ideal dinner you would like . . . compose a cricket eleven of the fattest men you know—you may manage six, the next three will be difficult; the last two perhaps impossible! And probably by then you will have gone to sleep, and anyway the "sex thought" will probably have quite disappeared.

Perhaps a boy may have the honesty to say: "But I *like* thinking and even talking about this subject!" Well, of course, I hope that on the whole Scouts keep off the topic, at any rate in talk; but if a boy says what I have just quoted, what of it? It simply means that he has the instinct that we have been talking about, and that the subject "attracts" him. If it didn't, there would be no problem! But it is like eating sugar. Sugar is sweet, and I like it. But a doctor tells me I have diabetes and mustn't eat sugar. He is not so silly as to tell me sugar wouldn't taste sweet *if* I ate it, or that I shall suddenly stop liking it; but *I* say: "Right! I'd like to—*but*—doctor's orders! So I won't!"

One last line about thoughts. Try not to imagine that almost anything is going to give you "sex" thoughts. Some boys are quite panicky about getting into "danger" because of what they hear or see. But Scouts usually have more common sense than that, and are tough. As they grow up, they will hear plenty; and perhaps see a good deal—you certainly are not going to be kept in a hot-house. Well, if you are practising control of your thoughts, you will be surprised how easy it becomes to think of what you choose. It is worth taking even ten minutes a day concentrating your attention on something —it doesn't matter what—and *determining* you will *not* be distracted by anything whatsoever—such as an aeroplane flying overhead. Don't look up! Or being offered a sweet. Take it; say Thank you, and *don't eat it* till the ten minutes are up. Your scalp tickles. Don't scratch it! You see the idea?

Now words. Words are spoken by you, or to you. *By* you—well, we may hope that a Scout keeps a clean tongue in his head. (At the same time, we haven't got to be priggish. In some circumstances men use "rough" words without meaning anything at all by them. They are a sort of "dialect": they may even be a way of keeping one's end up in horrible circumstances, like war. But that doesn't apply to you.) And even if a boy feels "A dirty story doesn't hurt *me*; I just laugh!" well, it *does* hurt him. It coarsens his mind a little. He probably tells it to *raise* a laugh—and there is an honest laugh, but also a nasty snigger. Again, others listening may say: "There! We're all the same! Scouts are tarred with the same brush! Scout A. was a bit of a hero to me, but now I see he's no better than the lowest of us." This disheartens the hero-worshipper. Besides, *you* may be tough (in the good sense), but some listener may be weak, and your story may be a real "temptation" to him.

Things said *to* you—I will take one or two examples of un-truths that you may hear; for I take it for granted that you will recognise openly "smutty" talk: but the lies might take you in.

(1) "Why try to be a freak? No one keeps quite 'good'!" This is not true. Many do. Others begin by being weak and then learn control. I have often heard boys of about sixteen in "uneducated classes" say: "I never done them things once I learned sense." Anyhow, the thing is to *try* not to lie down flat before so much as entering the ring! And getting knocked down doesn't matter so much, but staying down *does*.

(2) "Until you've done this or that, you've no experience. You're green." A half-truth! The man who gets that sort of experience has certainly *got* it; but you have a better one—the effects of self-control! You have got nearer to manhood; he, to animal-hood. He is left with the memory of a brief pleasure in the nerves; you go on possessing a lasting happiness in your mind and conscience, and the sense of having strengthened your will.

(3) "After all, it's only natural!" That again is a half-truth at best. Man's nature is like this—B. is the instinct part of him; A., his mind which controls instinct. If his nature were *only* B., he would be a mere animal. So it is *more* according to my "nature" to control my "B." with my "A." than to let my "B." just do as it pleases.

Should you try to stop "dirty" talk? It depends on (1) your personality—that is, if you are the sort of boy who *can*; and (2) on your position among your fellow-Scouts. You may not be the proper one to butt in. Anyhow, don't *add* to such talk. And, don't be too quick to think ill of those who use it. Oddly, those who talk the most are sometimes those who do the least.

Now about acts. Acts are done by yourself, or, with others. Self-abuse: I hope you can keep quite clear of this. If you like to keep your body clean in *every* way, and use lots of cold water, you will begin to like to keep it clean in the most important way of all. Try to take reasonable physical exercise, and (as I said) a Scout ought to have plenty with which to occupy his mind. But if you have got into a real *habit* (say, three or four times a week), aim at keeping clear of it for the first three days of the week, then start again, forgetting those three days, and keep clear for the next three days plus Sunday. And gradually you will get a whole week clear—always looking forward, and never back. Probably you will succeed for a bit and then fail. Never think: "There! It's no good! I am as bad as ever, and back where I started!" Not at all. If you have tried and succeeded for seven days, and fail on the eighth, you are seven days to the good so far as character-building goes. I repeat—look forward, not back; tell God you're sorry; ask Him quickly to help you; and then don't even pray about it. You don't want to keep your mind on the subject: if you *do* find you "brood," are puzzled, or despond, you would be wise to have one full frank talk with a trustworthy older man, but that ought to be enough. Catholics "go to confession," that is to say, tell their faults to someone who, they know, is experienced and cannot in any imaginable circumstances, even at risk of death, repeat what he has heard, and who will give good advice and encouragement. But after this, the fault must not become a topic of conversation. If a boy's difficulty be really great, he will be rightly advised to talk it over with a kindly doctor, who will be neither soft nor severe, and who understands the human mind.

You may notice that this "temptation" occurs when you feel depressed, lonely or bored, rather than when you are cheerful and occupied, and have companions, or, if you are restless and cannot sleep. In the first case, you are in an unlucky "mood," when you feel as if you didn't care what you did—anything for a change! This is the moment for great courage. If you possibly can, find a job of work, the harder the better: even do physical jerks for a bit, and get someone to talk to. And ask God to help you. But, and do notice this, if you can be master of your "moods," you can be master of anything! You will be a truly strong character. At night it is, of course, more awkward. Lie on your side: keep your arms crossed and your hands gently on your shoulders (this is very comfortable!) and start to think up your team of fat men or anything else. Don't say to yourself: "I *will* not—I *will* not do wrong," but, quite quietly, "I am not going to do anything I shouldn't." To struggle and twist, even in your mind, won't help you!

A boy may sometimes do such an action with another. This happens either because two small boys are thrilled at having a sort of secret and mystery that they share (but I hope that after this chapter there isn't much thrilling mystery left about the business); or because a smaller

35

boy gets a sort of hero-worship for an older one—this is quite a good thing provided he *is* worth being hero-worshipped!—or because a bigger boy makes a pet of a smaller one, in which case the small one oughtn't to feel flattered, but rather as if he were being treated like a little girl, and the older boy ought to know what a fool he looks. It is, too, possible for a boy just to want to teach wrong-doing to another, and that is a horrible thing, and must be altogether off the map so far as Scouts are concerned. I will say only this—*never* allow that to happen. It is doubly to mis-use the human body—his and yours: and you might even create a *habit of mind,* so that you would go on wanting that sort of thing, and then you would be in great danger of getting into trouble, even with the police, and risk sinking to having none but degraded companions, and end by being very lonely and useless. If there *is* a likelihood of this inclination becoming a habit, it would be right to talk it over with a wise doctor or other really trustworthy friend.

A couple of lines about girls. Young boys are not usually very interested in girls; but, as they grow up, they become more so; they are quite proud of being seen marching out with girls, and girls like having a "boy-friend," and the boy begins to dress up and the girl (quite possibly) to make-up, and they give one another presents and hold hands at cinemas, and go for a feed together, and let us hope that they both have good appetites. A boy can do pretty well at ices, sticky cakes, and fizzy drinks, but it is nothing to what a girl can. No ostrich has anything on their digestion. Well, that is all right, and quite natural; but there comes a moment when you will have to keep your heads, especially when you are of an age to feel romantic. Remember that harm done to a girl is far more serious than

"Ices, sticky cakes and fizzy drinks."

harm done to a boy, because the bodily and mental change in her goes deeper. Well, you must (1) control your *self* (as we have been saying all along), and (2) you must protect *her,* perhaps against herself, for she too has instincts and may be a weaker character than you. You want to respect and safeguard your girl, and all girls. Remember that she is probably some fellow's sister, and will probably be someone's wife. You would hate your sister, or your future wife, to have been ill-treated by all sorts of other men. A Scout ought to be *knightly* towards all women, old or young.

*　　*　　*　　*

I hope that neither you nor anyone else will have found anything soft or sentimental, or anything too easy-going, in this chapter. But you may have been surprised that I have hardly ever mentioned anything "religious." Well, I did not want to begin with that; but I certainly want to end with it. Scouts want to do their duty, and more than their strict duty, to every one of their fellow-men, to their country, and to God. We believe that God created us, and is preserving us, and means each of us to fulfil some special work in life that *no one else can.* But He has not given us an easy task. Anyhow, who wants to be given a soft job? Certainly not Scouts. Also, we have made it much harder for ourselves, owing to the fact that men have very often done what they know to be wrong, and still do so, and we ourselves, without doubt, do not always do what we know we should. This makes it harder for us to act rightly. So for many reasons I am *quite sure* that you will never really succeed in this matter of bodily self-control without the help of God. But to get it, we ought to ask for it; that is, to pray for it. Do not spend a long time praying about it, because that keeps your mind on the subject, which is just what we do not want. But say quickly: "God, help me!" and He certainly will.

Then if you know you have not done as well as you could, say quickly, but sincerely, "Dear Lord, forgive me. I am sorry, because You are so good: I resolve, with

Your help, not to do wrong again." Because, you know, that is true. God *is* good, and knows exactly how difficult things are for you and would much rather see His young son trying to run, even if he falls down, than not trying at all. But He expects you to pick yourself up (and He helps you to *get* up!) and to start again. But God has given us a very special help in the person of His Son, our Lord Jesus Christ. He was truly "man" as we are— in fact, He was once a boy of exactly your age and knows all about us "from the inside," so to say. He had His Mother, and His home, His work, and His play. I am sure that you would like to be the very best that your own mother, or your closest friend, would like you to be; in the same way, we can try to keep from saying or doing anything that our Lord and *His* Mother would not like to hear or watch. And no doubt some day many of you will go to Holy Communion. That means getting into as close touch with Him as you could be with your very closest friend, and even closer. So you will do better than just trying *not* to hurt or grieve Him—you will try to *please* Him and be as like Him as possible. It is always better to try to do right than just try not to do wrong!

So I ask God's blessing on this chapter and upon each one of you, that you may put up a fine fight for God and your neighbour, the first victory you carry off being over all that is less good in yourselves. It will be a hard struggle, now and then, but, God helping, you will win.

[*With Ecclesiastical approbation.*]

Chapter 4

PHYSICAL FITNESS

MANY and varied are opinions concerning Physical Fitness as are the sources from which they emanate. In many cases it is a matter of considerable difficulty to distinguish the wheat from the chaff, though few will find it hard to agree with the gentleman, notorious for his outspokenness, who says—one would hesitate to state he believes—"If you are well, you don't require exercise, if ill you can't take it."

As a Senior Scout you have reached the age—indeed, you have reached what is probably one of the most crucial stages in your journey through life—when you are called upon to make decisions, many of which will be for you, and you alone, to decide. Advice and help will be available for you to assist in making a correct choice, if you make an effort to seek it, and, what is more important, if you are big enough to accept it.

In venturing to offer advice on the subject of Physical Fitness, perhaps it would be as well to establish at the outset my own belief that my subject is, and can only be, if considered rationally, a means to an end. International rivalry in the sporting sphere is spotlighting more and more the fact that present-day athletes and sportsmen can no longer rely on natural ability, only the superbly trained can hope to compete and survive in these highly competitive days. Such training calls for sacrifice and hard work, but it is not my intention in this chapter to dwell on the rigorous schedules which

"Only the superbly trained can hope to survive."

are the lot of those who are ambitious in scaling the sporting heights—whether it be inclusion in an Everest team, participation in the Olympic Games, scoring the winning try at Twickenham, the winning run at the Oval in the final deciding Test—the choice is legion. Indeed, the present trend, many would argue, is retrograde, and doing little to support the opinion that it is the game which matters, not the result. Be that as it may, and without wishing to take sides in the argument, I have mentioned it if only for two reasons. Firstly, it is to draw attention to the fact that, where physical achievement is concerned, there can be little or no worth while result without hard work—as in any other branch of life. You can only hope to get out of a thing what you are prepared to contribute. Secondly, if hard and sustained training is essential for success in sport or any particular game or activity, how important is it that we should consider our physical fitness and well-being for the one game we all must play and which none can avoid—life itself?

I would like to submit that each and every one of us should, to the utmost of our ability, develop our talents so that we may not only enjoy the fruits of our labour,

"A cycle lacking grease is agony to ride."

but contribute largely to the enjoyment and well-being of those with whom we live, work and play. In this mechanical age we are easily dissatisfied with the engine which is not firing on all cylinders, a cycle lacking grease is agony to ride, a fault in a flying machine can have disastrous results. Yet in our own bodies we possess a more wonderful, efficient and intricate piece of machinery than any yet devised by man. Inwardly we are an engine of unique design; our brain, heart, etc., being the power unit, and our limbs with the accompanying muscles so arranged that we are able to perform movements of infinite variety. I would like to carry this analogy one step further and add simply, just as we seek trouble if we neglect our man-made mechanical devices, so it is with our own wonderful possession.

Can we then accept the fact that without regular care and attention our bodies cannot hope to function efficiently. The mere absence of illness does not necessarily mean that we are fit. We can roughly divide each day we live into three parts: a period for work; a period for leisure and play; a period for sleep. And what an important part our standard of physical fitness plays in all three! Whatever the job of work to be done, at the office, the bench, in the shop, are the tasks cheerfully accepted and performed with a willing spirit? In our leisure do we pursue our hobby intelligently or play our game wholeheartedly? Is our sleep deep—unaided by modern drugs—and the type from which we awaken refreshed and eager to face the challenge of a new day? If you can honestly say that you do welcome each day with its tasks, that you do enjoy refreshing sleep, then the chances are you know what fitness really is and have probably enjoyed the thrill of a race well run—not necessarily won—the pleasure of a hot bath after a hard-fought game on the sports field, the view as you rest after a successful attack on a rock face, that best-of-all meals cooked

"The pleasure of a hot bath."

on an open fire after a long trek, or perhaps the exhilarating feeling after a good sharp walk on a frosty morning.

In other words, and reversing the argument, if you have enjoyed healthy, vigorous exercise, then each day is more likely to be a welcome challenge, and sleep comes easily.

During your school life your opportunities for healthy exercise were ample. Both in the gymnasium and on the games field your periods were well planned, in addition to which your working day was comparatively short and your holidays long. It is when you leave school the problems arise. Your working hours are longer, you find yourself in a job where you have to spend a long time at a desk or a bench and further valuable time is eaten up with travelling. As a result, at times it requires a considerable effort to find opportunity to continue with some active, healthy, physical exercise. And, oh, so easy to join the swollen ranks of those who watch—and there is plenty to watch in these days of commercialised sport, not to mention the entertainment on tap through TV, Radio and the Cinema.

I am the last to join those who decry all these modern aids to inactive leisure. On the contrary, I welcome them. Particularly if our young people can learn to make use of them intelligently. Confining ourselves to the sporting aspects, what better than that there should be wider opportunity of seeing the really expert perform. What lessons of technique we can learn and what inspiration can be gained if we allow our imagination to be fired and we have the will-power to get on with something ourselves! In any case, why should anyone deprive those unfortunate people stricken with illness, or the aged left with only happy memories of their more active days, of entertainment? Certainly not because some young people are too idle to bestir themselves into activity more becoming of their age and physical condition.

This business of healthy exercise is every bit as much mental as well as physical discipline. Once you take the easy way out it becomes a very much harder task to apply yourself again to strenuous activities.

I readily admit that it is quite often both difficult and awkward to find time and opportunity to indulge in a physical activity, but I equally assert that all of us, to our own taste and choice, are the richer, not only for the enjoyment of participation or glory of achievement, but because we made the effort.

Can we, therefore, briefly examine the opportunities

42

which exist and a few principles we might employ to ensure that at least physically, and as a result largely mentally, we are able to function efficiently?

As a Scout you have had an unrivalled introduction to many activities which by their very nature are ideal for their health and fitness promoting possibilities. These are activities which we can continue to enjoy all our days. All of us who have at some time or other camped, hiked, trekked, sailed or taken part actively in outdoor pursuits will remember with affection some veteran who has been joining in the fun for countless years. Of people like E. G. Rowland who, on retirement as a Civil Servant, climbed forty-nine peaks of 2,000 feet and over in Snowdonia between his sixty-fourth and sixty-eighth birthdays, and completed his half-century a few days after his sixty-eighth birthday. I am reminded even as I write—during a camping holiday near a Cornish cove—by the arrival of two charming ladies to spend a few days under canvas. They both cheerfully admit to being "well on the wrong side of sixty" and tell me they started camping in 1925 and have even camped in the Rockies in Canada. Such is the appeal of the activities with which most Scouts are familiar which might prompt you to say, justifiably: "The answer is simple—encourage everybody to take up outdoor activities," and to which I should have to reply, "It's not really quite so easy as all that. You see, strangely enough, some people don't enjoy that type of physical recreation." There would appear to be no valid reason why there should not be, as there rightly is, a complete freedom of choice of game, sport or activity. The greater the choice the better, at the same time the lesser the excuse for not taking part.

It is said that some people play games to keep fit, others get fit to play games. Which is right? Personally, I would say there are virtues in both schools of thought. Let us examine for a moment two activities, say Camping and Hiking and Rugby Football. The average chap does not, generally speaking, camp regularly every weekend. Nor do weather conditions allow for regularity. Does he allow

himself to stagnate between excursions! Our Rugby footballer does evening training during the light nights at the
beginning of the season, but mostly during the season he
has to be satisfied with his weekly game to keep him
going. What is the answer to the problem posed here?
I would say the answer is largely contained in a commonsense approach to this entire subject of Physical Fitness.
I hesitate to put forward a set of rules just as much as
I'm afraid I shy from a "daily dozen."

I would require far more space than is at my disposal
if I were to fully discuss all the factors affecting sound
bodily health and fitness. Which immediately pin-points
one of my early statements that advice and help is available to you but *you* must make the effort. A wealth of
literature is available—if you feel your knowledge on any
point is inadequate, win your first and hardest battle by
seeking out the information.

To briefly review our field of discussion: firstly, there
is personal hygiene. Good, sound, regular habits are obviously essential as are the amount and type of food to be
eaten. Personally, I like to follow the training I received
as a youngster and largely accept "what is put on the
table." If I might permit myself a small "must" then I
would plump for fresh fruit and vegetables. The value of
showering, particularly after exercise, cannot be over-
emphasised. Suitable clothing, and in particular good,
sound footwear, also play their part. Fresh air and sun-
light are powerful aids to health and fitness, but here I
would make a plea for care and moderation when the
all-too-rare opportunities for sunbathing arise. I am sure
you all appreciate the value of a good night's sleep.

These first few points are common to us all, and, therefore, quite often we tend to neglect detail. A few late
nights, over-indulgence in food, even "waiting another
day for a bath," how many of us have been guilty of these
indiscretions? And without apparent ill-effects. Therein
lies the danger. It is so easy to develop bad habits that
I would stress that time, thought and action given to the
foregoing will pay handsome dividends. Indeed, I would

go further and say that if your daily routine cannot measure up to a decent standard, a lot of the positive action you take for physical fitness will be undermined. Before dealing with these positive steps I would quickly like to mention two other factors which to my mind are better grouped with our daily habits. I refer to smoking and drinking. The best advice I can give is "don't!" Smoking is a pleasant social habit and one so widely accepted these days that I would hesitate to be dogmatic with my advice. Whatever your inclination might be, it is as well to remember that most of the medical evidence available points to nicotine being harmful to the lungs, and most top-line athletes, certainly when in training, completely abstain. If one can suggest an open mind on the question of smoking, drink is in another category altogether. Alcohol is a poison, so the answer is, or should be, obvious. Yet here again social occasions and the "local" are such well-established institutions that it is often a matter of difficulty to be the "odd man out." A glass of beer after a hard day's work or a hard game may not do much harm, but . . . . So many lives have been ruined with alcohol that the moral is obvious. And remember, they all started with "just a glass of beer." It has been proved so effectively that alcohol reduces both mental and physical efficiency to such a degree that in no way can it contribute to physical fitness. In any case, the non-smoking and non-drinking man is a wiser, healthier and wealthier man.

In considering the more positive action we should take in the way of exercise, let us first of all see what good physical condition demands. Briefly, it calls for efficient muscles, good "wind" or respiratory system, a vigorous blood stream, which means a sound heart, arteries and veins, and reasonable posture. Each is interdependent.

How does one set about ensuring that each of these components is functioning correctly, and what amount of servicing is required to maintain them. Does the answer lie in one of the advertised "systems" which claim: "You, too, can have a body like mine!" The trouble is

YOU TOO CAN
HAVE A BODY LIKE ME

perhaps you don't want that type of body! Perhaps six golden rules that I could now give might be the answer—for some. No, I believe each individual should be left to work out his own salvation. To achieve success, all he requires is commonsense.

First and foremost—and here I have no hesitation in being dogmatic—each and every individual should be interested in, and, what is more important, should actively participate in some physical recreative activity. What it should be is your choice. There are so many games, sports and activities to choose from that there is no excuse for anyone to stand aside and watch. What should you consider when making your choice? I would advise: think in terms of enjoyment and don't worry for one moment about whether this game or that sport will do you more good. For many, and largely as a result of school training, ball games and the major sports provide the answer. If they do, it is probably because they were good enough to play in one of the teams. Those who didn't should search around and try something else—judo, fencing, archery, basket ball, squash, badminton, golf are a few suggestions. The open-air pursuits are well known to Scouts. There is in existence some activity which will appeal, and the opportunity for joining in is there if only you will search it out.

Having found your activity I believe you are more than halfway home. Yet, coming back to the question of whether the activity will keep you fit or whether you have to get fit for your activity, quite a lot will depend on the activity, what opportunities you have for taking part, and the standard of performance to which you aspire. There is no doubt that the better we can perform, the more enjoyment and benefit we derive. This in turn calls for considerable effort and sometimes hard work in mastering techniques, which is popularly known as training. You

46

will obviously seek advice from the expert coaches in the activities of your choice, but your everyday activities can assist enormously, and, what is more, form habits which will reap dividends long after your active playing days are behind you. The simplest, and these days the most neglected aid to health, is walking. The number of cars and public service vehicles available for us encourage laziness. A few minutes each day spent walking instead of riding— and I mean really stepping out, arms swinging out—are a fine investment for health. Then, again, we spend so much time sitting at a desk, in a car, or bending over a bench or machine that through time we lose the upright stance that is the hallmark of good posture. A daily look in a mirror

"A few minutes spent walking instead of riding."

will soon reveal if you are beginning to develop the minor deformities which are the penalties of our highly-civilised life. The real danger signs are shoulders beginning to round, thus cramping the activity of your lungs, and signs of a "corporation."

You can find many types of exercises which will counteract these twin evils, but a simple tip is to try, whenever you can remember, and whether you be sitting or standing, to make yourself taller by pushing up the top and back of your head. Try it, and see how it lifts your chest wall, squares your shoulders, tightens your abdominal muscles. Something you can do one hundred times a day.

"Pushing up the top and back of your head."

I have deliberately refrained from giving you a list of exercises designed to cure, because I firmly believe that there is more virtue in seeking out your own requirements than in blindly accepting a quack

47

remedy. In any case, requirements differ according to build, temperament, living conditions, and a host of other factors. That we should participate in some physical recreative activity is essential, that we need some supplementary exercise to prepare for it I feel is equally important. First, to counteract our living and working conditions—as it were, remedial exercise; second, that we may better enjoy our activity by improved performance—training. To what extent you carry out each phase is your decision. On the one hand, you require enough to retain a silhouette you can be proud of. On the other, it is a matter of what standard you desire to attain. Just think of the long hours the concert pianist spends at scales and finger exercises: the four-minute-miler has to work just as hard. If you can scale the heights, by all means do so, but remember you can, each of you, attain your own Everest according to your ability. And just one word to those who through illness or accident are prevented from following the routine paths to health through physical activity. A visit to one of the famous rehabilitation centres would soon convince you that ingenuity and endeavour can produce wonderful results and a magnificent sense of achievement for those who have conquered.

So far I have been careful to avoid, as far as possible, particular do's and don'ts. I wish to make an exception now and make a plea that everyone should be able to swim. Not only because it is a means of getting first-class exercise and enjoyment, but in the hope that it might help to halt the appalling loss of life which takes place each year through drowning. We live on a small island with an abundance of lakes, rivers and streams, and, if it is right that we should take advantage of these wonderful natural facilities, then it is equally proper that we should prepare adequately to use them.

In conclusion, may I say a few words about the enjoyment of physical activities by virtue of helping others. In other words, through leadership or coaching. Whatever your game, sport or activity, you will inevitably, whatever your standard of performance, if you apply yourself intelligently and enthusiastically to it, amass a wealth of knowledge and experience. And in the process you will have good reason to be thankful to one or more people for the help, advice and encouragement they have been able to offer. What better thanks can you give than to carry on in the same tradition. One might almost suggest that it is a duty to do so, particularly if you have the aptitude, patience and love of people which are the basic ingredients of a good coach or leader. If you are not suited for this side, perhaps your contribution can be on the administration side. Failing all else, at least by your enthusiasm you can encourage others to join you and thus be well on the way to enjoying a fuller, richer life and really live, not merely exist.

Chapter 5

THE WORLD YOU LIVE IN

"The world you live in."

TO be wakened in the middle of the night to learn that your father was being taken away by the secret police, and might never be seen alive again; to know that Scouting, and the holding of the views on which Scouting is based, were forbidden, under most severe penalties; to be compelled either to give away your family and friends to the secret police, or to face torture and imprisonment not only for yourself but for them; to know that any of the grand people who were your friends and leaders might at any moment be imprisoned, or worse, without trial and without having committed any crime except to defy a corrupt and tyrannical government—these are the terrors that, mercifully, strike us as fantastic and impossible, and yet we know, if we stop to think, that just such things can and do happen in other parts of the world, and have happened in the lifetime of many of us, over vast parts of our own continent of Europe.

When we try to imagine life against such a background, it is so utterly different from everything we are accustomed to that it is quite impossible even to begin to feel what the victims of those conditions must feel, and our own grouses and difficulties become so trivial as to make us quite ashamed ever to have complained at them.

"Our own grouses and difficulties become trivial."

50

But the contrast does not end there. Not only have we no experience of a life of oppression, but we feel as sure that we are free from any risk of it as we are sure that the sun will rise tomorrow (although, of course, we may feel nearly as sure that it will not be visible in England for many minutes!)

Less than fifty years ago—when Scouting was already born—the lives of other nations were remote from life in this country. Now, radio, television and air-travel have brought the whole world so much closer together than even our parents would have dreamed, in their youth, to be possible, and these changes have made the well-being and manner of life of other peoples vitally important to us, for at least three compelling reasons.

First, the trade, commerce and industry of our own country, on which our means of living a decent life so much depend, are bound up with the supply of raw materials from, and the markets provided by, countries in every part of the globe.

Secondly, just because travel is so fast and so easy, any crisis or warfare, no matter how remote in actual distance, is more than likely to spread and develop so as to threaten all the values that make our normal way of life the worthwhile thing that it is.

Finally, and surely most important, if we have anything of the true spirit of Scouting about us, we simply cannot sit back and not care that other folk are suffering untold misery, not even because they deserve it, but because of the very fact that they share our own ideas of what is good and worthwhile in life.

Why is it, then, that we are free from these dangers, and can feel free, too, from the fear of them? This is not a mere theoretical question, for to preserve our liberties and our way of life is impossible unless we know what makes them not only possible, but secure. It has been said, very truly, that "the price of liberty is eternal vigilance"; whether we, and the generations of the future, go on enjoying it must depend on the extent to which we continue to guard and preserve it. This we cannot begin

51

to do until we know, and value, the things on which it is based.

To understand what those things are, we have to look far back into our history. Magna Carta is not just a picturesque event in history—it is still, in many senses, the very foundation of the freedom we enjoy. It is not easy to think of the struggle that led to this Charter as something intensely real and human, vitally affecting the lives of the people of this island ever since—but it was just that.

"Magna Carta is not just a picturesque event in history."

It gave the right and the power to govern this country to Parliament, and there the right and the power have remained. Needless to say, it was by no means recognisable as what we now understand by Parliament, for our modern Parliament—like all worthwhile English institutions—is the result of a gradual growth over the years.

The story of the struggle between King and Parliament, especially in the Stuart period, is another piece of history that is fascinating when you appreciate that it was a vital stage on the way to the present situation, in which the relations between our Queen, on the one hand, and the peoples of the Commonwealth and their Parliaments on the other, are so soundly based in affection that it is very hard to visualise a monarch in this country at war with his people.

It is Parliament, consisting of the two Houses, of Lords and of Commons, that makes and revises our laws, imposes the taxes to pay for our public services, and is responsible for aspects of our lives as varied as the provision of education from babyhood onwards, the maintenance of the Armed Forces, and the provision of hospitals, pensions, sickness benefits and other means of preventing hardship in times of misfortune.

52

The fundamental feature of the House of Commons is, of course, that its members are all elected by the votes of the people. Every adult citizen is entitled to vote, and it is a tragedy that a great many of them do not take the trouble to use this right, which is one of the foundations of true democracy.

The place of the House of Lords in our democratic system is an interesting study. Its members are not elected, but have the right to sit, and vote, in the House of Lords because they are peers (except in the case of certain of the Bishops, who occupy a special position as representatives of the Church). Their powers have been very much curtailed in the course of history, and particularly in our own century. The whole future of the House of Lords—whether it has a place in a democracy; if so, what that place shall be; and what reforms are desirable in regard to it—is a question that has long been discussed, and is likely to be decided in your lifetime as an elector. It may very well be a major issue at some General Elec-

tion when you have the opportunity (and the duty) to vote, so it is important that you should find out what the arguments are and make up your mind, so as to play a responsible part in the future of our country.

General Elections are normally held about every five years, and then the whole of the existing M.P.s, or members of the House of Commons, cease to hold that position and an entirely new House of Commons is elected— although, of course, it usually contains a substantial proportion

"... cease to hold that position."

of the former members. As the elections are conducted on Party lines, practically no successful candidate being independent of the major political parties, it is essential to know what the principal parties stand for. In this

53

country there are now only two parties with large numbers of members in the House—the Conservative (or Tory) and the Labour (or Socialist)—but the Liberal Party is well worth studying, despite the fact that its numbers are much smaller. We have had an occasional Communist M.P., and representatives of one or two other minority viewpoints, but the contribution that they make to the political outlook of the country is not a significant one.

In a single chapter such as this, I cannot attempt to do justice to the political philosophy of any party; what I do want to emphasise is that certain commonly-held ideas about politics are childish, and unworthy of anyone who really intends to do his best to do his duty to his country. First, there is the attitude that politics is not my business —it is obvious that if every fair-minded person took that view, the country would be in the control of the diehards and extremists. Next, there is the line that leads people to say, "A statesman is a leader in my Party—a politician is a leader in any other party"—so closing their minds to the good that, surely, every political party must include in its outlook, and being guided by prejudice and not by sound judgment. Finally, there is a dangerous viewpoint taken by some otherwise sensible and responsible people— the view that modern political affairs are too complicated for the man in the street to understand, and so it is impossible for him to take sides at all. This is unsound; I know very little about nuclear fission, but I do know for what purposes it ought to be used, and it is questions of principle such as that, and not the underlying technical matters, on which elections are, and should be, decided.

A General Election having taken place, the carrying out of the policy of the party that has obtained a majority in the new House of Commons is the responsibility of the Cabinet, which is in effect a committee of the Government, or majority party. It is characteristic of our British way of doing things that both the Cabinet and the office of Prime Minister as head of it and of the Government, grew up informally and without any official establishment by Act of Parliament, and yet occupy key positions in the life of the country. Here, again, the story of their development is an absorbing one.

Once elected, an M.P. is the representative not of the members of his party, but of all the people of the constituency from which he was elected. But he is not their delegate, for he has a duty to exercise his own judgment on all matters on which he is called upon to vote in the House.

Although Parliament is the supreme law-making body, for this purpose it comprises not only the two Houses of Parliament, but also the Crown, with the result that no Bill passed by those two bodies becomes an Act, and so part of the law, until it has received the Royal Assent. Since, however, ours is a constitutional monarchy (governed by the law of the land), and not an absolute one (in which the ruling monarch is all-powerful), and since also the Crown is above politics, the Royal Assent is always given, if the Cabinet so advises the Queen.

The law of the constitution, which makes ours a constitutional monarchy and has contributed so much to the smooth working of our Parliamentary system, is as interesting in itself as it is important in its results.

First, it is a striking fact that the constitution of this country is not a written one, like, for example, that of the United States of America. Once again, it is something which has grown out of our English way of life, has developed with a changing social set-up, and yet is as clearly defined and as certain as any written code.

Moreover, it binds and protects everyone, from the Crown to the most humble citizen, and ensures to all that no law shall be made, no right interfered with, except by the proper use of our democratic machinery.

Finally—although this does not exhaust the subject, which I must however leave before it exhausts you—our constitutional law reserves to the Crown certain very important prerogatives, and yet controls the way in which they shall be exercised, so as to ensure that in regard to them the monarch acts on the advice of the Ministers, or Cabinet.

Of these, two deserve special mention—foreign policy, and the prerogative of mercy. Parliament can, and of course, does, debate foreign policy, but in law it is the Crown, on the advice of the Cabinet, that decides upon it. The prerogative of mercy enables the Crown—on the advice of the Home Secretary—to grant a reprieve or pardon to a person who has been sentenced by the Courts. In other words, whilst the Crown cannot punish except through the Courts, and does not interfere with the trial of a prisoner, it can and does show mercy in suitable cases, which is of enormous value in our system which, in some cases such as murder, gives the trial judge no discretion but to pass sentence of death, no matter how great the mitigating circumstances of the case.

To return to the way in which the country is governed, it is obvious that Parliament cannot do more than settle the general policy in regard to most of the social and other services which it provides, and within the broad framework of that policy, many of them are administered by local authorities. These, again, form part of our democratic system, and are elected by the adult population—or, to be more exact, by as many of that population as do their duty.

The County Borough Councils, in large urban areas, manage all local public affairs, such as schools, police, fire service and libraries; the County Councils, Borough (or Town) Councils, Urban and Rural District Councils, and Parish Councils, all have a very real influence and effect on the daily lives of the population of their areas, by whom, and from amongst whom, they are elected. Their services are given without payment (other than out-of-pocket expenses), and their integrity, good sense, and willingness to face public criticism form one of the bulwarks of free democracy.

Just as fundamental as the making of laws is the enforcement of them, and for this purpose we have judges who are completely independent of politics, and before whom all men are equal. Since the last War, we have seen the advent of a system of legal aid that provides professional legal help for all who could not otherwise afford it, and although Parliament provides the funds to make this possible, the granting of legal aid in any individual case is in no way controlled by the Government.

One of the vital functions of the Courts is to preserve our freedom of thought, of speech, and of meeting. Once again, there is no written law laying down these fundamental freedoms, but the Common Law of England, developed over the centuries, safeguards them. Nevertheless, we have to bear always in mind that what the law gives, new law can take away—and so the democratic control in Parliament is essential to these great privileges that are part of our heritage. If anything I have written in this chapter has caused you to think afresh about your reading of history, read again something about the history of freedom of religious worship in this country, and you will see how much we owe to the courageous souls of former times, and therefore how great our responsibility is, to them and to those who come after us, to preserve what by their sacrifices they won.

So far, I have written almost exclusively about our own country. It is equally fascinating to look farther afield; to discover how, from the conquests and discoveries from the former Elizabethan days onwards, there has grown up the British Commonwealth of Nations, largely and ever-increasingly self-governing, yet bound together by a very real tie of loyalty. The process of development can be studied, from life, by a comparison of the old-established Dominions of Canada and Australia with the newly-created India and Pakistan, or with Central Africa, now at the crossroads.

Nearer home, the new democracy in Germany is not just interesting, but an institution whose success or failure could play a fatal part in the peace of the world. We have probably all met Germans—possibly German Scouts—been impressed with their similarity to ourselves in much of their outlook and character, and then asked ourselves how such a race could have submitted to, and by their submission made possible, the tyranny of Hitler and

57

Nazism. To begin to understand this needs some knowledge of Germany's history—made up of small kingdoms
and principalities, independent and jealous of one another;
united only in war; defeated in the First World War, and
failing tragically in her first real experiment in democracy,
between the Wars, under the Weimar Republic. Here,
again, history is not an affair of dates, of battles, but the
intensely human story of a people, and if ever you have
an opportunity to hear it told by a German who cares
passionately for the success of his country's new experiment in democracy, do not miss it.

Of Russia, with a political system based on a single
party, and on a philosophy in which God is denied, and
of the many other challenging problems of the world
today, I cannot write in one short chapter, but that does
not mean that they are any the less deserving of our
serious study and attempt to understand them.

If you have read as far as this, it is a proof that you
are prepared to do some serious thinking, and in the belief
that you will go on doing so, I will make a few suggestions as to what I believe our job as Scouts to be.

With our faith in God as the Father of us all, and so
in the brotherhood of all His children, with the clear
challenge of our Scout Promise, and the plain signposts
of the Scout Law, we should be less than true Scouts if
we did not play our part in preserving our democratic way
of life, and helping others to achieve it according to their
own pattern.

To do this involves, as in all worthwhile Scouting,
training for the job in hand. As we enjoy the benefits our
country provides for us, as we see something of other
lands, as we meet people of other nations, let us make it
our business not just to see what is on the surface, but
to decide what is good and of permanent worth, how it
comes to be and how it can be preserved and developed;
what is lacking, why it is lacking, and how the need is
to be overcome; and what we as individuals, and as
members of a community in which we have a larger voice

as we grow older, can do to play, in the life of our town, our country, our Commonwealth and the world, a part worthy of a true Scout.

Chapter 6

THE QUEEN'S SCOUT BADGE

THE Queen's Scout Badge is the highest Scout proficiency award. This being so, it is, of course, difficult and demands knowledge and ability in many Scouting subjects. Note the term "Scouting subjects." These are the things that are the flesh and blood of practical Scouting. There are many badges to encourage hobbies and other activities, but these do not qualify for the Queen's Scout Badge.

A Scout starts to train and qualify for this Badge as soon as he is invested. You must be a Tenderfoot to get the Second Class—which is a requirement for the First Class Badge. The First Class Badge, the Bushman's Thong or the Air or Sea equivalent and four Public Service Badges are necessary to gain the Queen's Scout Badge.

"So many things to do."

In these days of so many things to do, it is necessary to think out beforehand exactly what you wish to achieve, how long it will take, and in which order to attack the project. How many of us wish and hope to do something without really attempting to think things out to ensure good progress and success? Success is rarely achieved by luck. It's wanting something sufficiently to work hard and purposefully with energy towards the target you have set yourself. That is very true of those who want success in gaining their Queen's Scout Badge.

Here are some ideas on how to attack the job of gaining the Queen's Scout Badge. First of all you should try to get the First Class Badge. This is just common sense and a moderate ability to be practical. There are a number of booklets on this Badge, and I won't repeat them here.

There is no order in which you should get the Bushman's Thong and Public Services Badges, except that the wise Senior Scout will make good use of the summer months to polish off the Bushman's Thong ones.

The Bushman's Thong qualifications are to hold the First Class Badge, the Venturer Badge and two of the following: Camp Warden, Forester, Naturalist, Meteorologist, Senior Pioneer, Hiker, Tracker or Astronomer, but not both Astronomer and Meteorologist. Many of these badges require that the under-15 equivalent should be passed or re-passed. If you hold one of these, you have already passed a large part of the Badge.

The best plan is to pair up with another Senior Scout and, together, make up your minds which badges you will get. Instructors are not always easy to find. Remember that there are many excellent people ready to help if they are asked. I know one Senior Scout who wanted his Meteorologist Badge. By asking a number of people, he found a member of the Royal Meteorological Society living within easy reach of him who was delighted to be asked to help. I know this looks easy in print! That

"Instructors are not easy to find."

is where tenacity of purpose comes in. If your Scouter cannot find an instructor, perhaps the local schoolmaster or policeman or some local society may be able to give suggestions—depending on the subject. The important thing is not to give in because it looks difficult. The Queen's Scout Badge is a great challenge. If you accept the challenge, then you must *be prepared* to overcome all frustrations and difficulties.

Write down the badges you intend to get. Put them in

61

the order you will attempt them. Decide on the target date you will set yourself for each badge. Make your decisions after careful thought, and then go ahead determined to turn your plans into achievements.

It may help you to know that many Districts and Camp Sites run Badge Instruction Courses for the more specialised badges. Take advantage of these if you can, but don't be afraid of learning by trying things out for yourself.

I'm now going to take you into my confidence. Like so many Scouters, I don't really like admitting that a great

"Trying things out on your own."

deal of my Scouting knowledge was gained by trying things out on my own, learning by mistakes and then giving instruction on the subject as if I was the fountainhead of all wisdom!

A Scouter often has to learn up things with nobody to give him instruction. If a Scouter can do this—why not you? Don't think by this that I mean knowledge gained solely from books, but a combination of informed "know-how" and practical skill gained by experience.

There are booklets to help you on all the Bushman's Thong, Seaman's, Airman's and Public Service Badges. It will, however, depend entirely on you. It will also take time.

The Public Service Badges required are the Ambulance Badge and three of the following: Air Observer, Civics, Conservation, Despatch Rider, Fireman, Handyman, Interpreter, Leading Signaller, Pathfinder, Pilot, Public Health and Rescuer.

So much for the badges required to gain the Queen's Scout Badge. You already know that this will need grit and determination as well as knowledge and ability, but all these qualities would be useless unless each Queen's Scout was a shining example of what a good Scout should be. I think it would be impossible to devise a test to ensure that each Queen's Scout really understood and practised the Scout Promise and Law in his everyday life—but obviously he would be unworthy if he did not set a very high example to all other Scouts. This is one of the heavy responsibilities that rest on the shoulders of all who gain this highest award.

Our rules state that "a Queen's Scout is one who, having thoroughly trained himself in Scoutcraft, places that training at the disposal of the community for public service." This means that you must undertake to use your knowledge for the good of others. That's why Scout training is so important and worthwhile. In our Movement we don't learn things to pass examinations—we learn things to help others, and wear a badge to show them we have been trained in that subject.

Every Queen's Scout will receive a Royal Certificate signed by H.M. the Queen. This was specially designed for the purpose and was personally approved by the Queen, who has been an active member of our sister Movement, the Girl Guides, and is our Patron. The Chief Scout holds receptions for the presentation of these certificates.

A Queen's Scout may justifiably be proud of his achievements, and many people unconnected with our Movement recognise that a Scout who has gained this award has something which the average chap lacks. In industry and commerce and the Services, a Queen's Scout is expected to be especially efficient, reliable and responsible, and, as such, is often given opportunities not offered to others who do not hold this qualification.

So now you must make up your own mind. My advice is: try hard for it, accept the challenge, and whether you succeed or not you will be all the better for the attempt. Good luck to you!

Chapter 7

THE SENIOR SCOUT AND HIS PLACE IN THE MOVEMENT

LET us assume to begin with that you are in one of those lucky Groups who have a Senior Scout Troop or at least a Senior Patrol and good and capable Senior Scouters. It is assuming a lot, for many of our Groups have neither, and there seems little point in sprouting maroon epaulettes when there is no one to lead and nowhere to lead to. In that case you would surely be happier leading your old Patrol in the Boy Scout Troop, where at least you were busy and happy.

Even if you are one of the lucky Groups, you may part with that Patrol with great regret, and I sympathise with your feelings. They were your first independent command and as precious to you as a ship to her captain. There is nothing in life quite so thrilling or so solemn as the moment you first know that others are looking to you for leadership and that you must not fail them.

"Your first independent command."

But you see there are many who ought to have that thrill and responsibility and, while you are blocking the way, they will not have a chance.

So we ask you now to leave that patrol you have built up so proudly and give young David a chance. You trained him, so you know he will make a job of it.

He may not lead as well as you at first, and you may

feel the urge to go back and sort things out for yourself when they seem in a jumble. But resist that temptation and leave him to it, unless he asks for your advice and help, for, like you, he will only learn by making mistakes.

In any case, you are going to be far too busy to worry about the Owls any more. You have a hectic Scout programme leading to your Queen's Scout Badge to fit in somehow, and adventurous and exciting outdoor activities which you were not strong enough or big enough to tackle in the Troop. You have the chance of attending one or more of the great International Jamborees and finding out for yourself that, whatever the papers may say, the Scouts of all nations are grand fellows at heart who want nothing so much as to live in peace and friendship with you. And you may be lucky enough to experience one or two of those smaller international camps of thirty or forty fellows from two or three nations, where you seem to get even deeper into the heart of international friendship than at the great gatherings. Don't miss the chance of camping abroad as much as you can in the next year or two, even if you have to scrape the barrel as far as money is concerned, in order to do so. You are not properly educated until you have seen for yourself how your brother Scouts live, and what their countries look like.

People will tell you that you don't need to go out of England to see beautiful things, and they are right as far as they go, for there is no land on earth like this one of ours. But you are lucky enough to have time stretching away before you to a very far horizon, and there will be plenty of time to see England later, when you are too tied up with responsibilities to get far afield. Now is the time to spread your wings and see the world. It may never come again.

So go abroad as much as you can and meet your brother Scouts of other lands, and do it the hard way—with a rucksack and a lightweight tent on your back. There are two reasons for this. The first is that it will be easier on your pocket that way, and the second that only by doing

c

so can you really get to know a country and its people.

International Scouting should be very prominent on your menu for the next year or two. Your own D.C. and the International Department at I.H.Q. are there to help and advise you about the details of your journeys.

One last word on this subject. Wherever you go, people will judge Scouting by your behaviour as a representative of the land where Scouting was born. You must never forget that, and never forget also that you are travelling among proud peoples, and that if their ways and habits seem strange to you, yours are equally strange to them and just as amusing at times.

Of course, international adventures will only form a small part of your Senior Scouting, most of which will have to be done in the more humdrum atmosphere of normal work or school. As a First Star Wolf Cub you had one eye open, and later, as a Two Star Cub, both eyes. Then, in the Troop, you gambolled about in the valleys learning elementary things about life. Now you have climbed to the hilltops and life is spread out below you like a stretch of country full of forests, lakes and rivers and all sorts of fascinating paths for you to explore. Your horizon is ever widening and you have all sorts of interests that you did not have a year or so ago.

Scouting must give way a bit to admit those other interests and activities and must not clash with them, and yet we hope it will continue to occupy a permanent corner in your life.

But you must not let it get out of proportion in relation

"Tussling with the certificate of education."

with the other things you are doing. There are more important things in life than Scouting, and we do not want any more fanatics in the Movement. We have enough already.

If you are still at school, you will be tussling with the certificate of education at either the General or Advanced level, and

66

that must come first, for the whole of your future life may hinge on your success.

If you are working you are building up knowledge and experience, and winning the confidence and trust of your firm, and that must come first also.

Then you may find that you have an increasing interest in the youth club or dramatic society attached to your church, and maybe the interest is not confined to drama and youth club activities, for you will be mixing socially with some very jolly girls. That must have its corner also. All these things are part of life and of a balanced personality, and that is what we hope you are going to be.

Your Scouters know that, and will not expect you to spend too much time in active Scouting, but they will expect that in the limited time you have left you will do your Scouting with all your might.

The journey through the Senior badges to your Queen's Scout Badge is packed with interest, and is within the reach of many more of you than complete it at present. It seems a pity, when you have gone so far along the Scouting trail, not to finish the job off properly with the Queen's Scout Badge and a visit to Windsor Castle for the St. George's Day Parade and Service.

There is nothing like finishing a job properly.

"It is not the beginning, but the continuing to the end until it be thoroughly finished, wherein lieth the true glory."

But remember that the decision to finish the job properly, and the determination to do it, now rests

"You are past the stage when you should need prodding."

with you. You are past the stage when you should need prodding and harrying to enter and prepare for a badge test. That may have been necessary at times in the Owls when you were an irresponsible young Second Class Scout, but not in the Wingate Patrol.

Here the drive must come from you, not your Scouters, or else all the years we have been teaching you initiative and self-reliance have been wasted.

In your outdoor Scouting you may find that you have a flair for rock climbing or pot-holing or other pursuits which would have turned your S.M. grey while you were in the Troop. It is right that you should do these slightly hazardous things now, for a little danger is the salt to season the dish for anyone who calls himself a man. But remember there is nothing manly in being foolhardy and taking unjustifiable risks or attempting something for which you are not fully trained. And if you are the leader in an unprepared enterprise, it is worse than foolhardy— just plain bad leadership, because the lives of others are involved.

Oddly enough, though you may appear revolting objects to mankind as a whole, to three or four people, especially to your mother, you are still things precious and of great worth. Why it should be so is one of the great mysteries of life!

Those two great military leaders, the Duke of Wellington and Lord Montgomery, always won their battles for the same reason. There was no luck about their success. They never started until they were quite ready and had something up their sleeve to meet any unexpected development which might occur.

That is the way to start any adventure where danger may be lurking for those who leave things to chance.

Of course, your flair may be for bird-watching or zoology or something less hazardous and less nerve-wracking for your Scouters, but just as enjoyable.

In general, you will find camping on permanent camp sites, however beautiful, to be very tame stuff nowadays. This sort of camping is for the tenderfeet and not for you. For you the lightweight tent or brushwood shelter, the hiking camp or trek, the expedition with a purpose, on difficult ground or on the mountain track. Do not waste precious time lounging about laid-on camp sites, for you have more to do than you can possibly fit in, and to waste time is the ultimate sin. There is never enough of it and, at your age, you should almost grudge the time you spend sleeping.

"Begrudge the time you spend sleeping!"

You may be becoming bewildered at all the manifold things you are expected to fit into a fourteen-hour working day, and indeed they are manifold.

I would list them as follows in order of priority:—

(1) Duty to God by attendance at your church.

(2) Duty to your parents and home by becoming an active partner in it and paying back a fraction of the debt you owe to them.

(3) Duty to yourself by mastering your profession or job.

(4) First spare-time activity—Senior Scouting, international journeys, adventurous camping, and outdoor pursuits.

(5) Youth club, social activities, playing games, reading.

(6) Padding for odd moments—watching games, chasing girls, theatres, good films, television, radio, eating, drinking (soft only), and sleep.

If you do these things in this order with all your might you will be an acquisition to any Senior Scout Patrol. But keep them in order, for the ones you enjoy most have a habit of jumping the queue if you do not watch them.

It is hard to see how you could fit more in, but there is one other thing you might consider. For four or five years your Scouters have been hard at work to produce a Senior Scout, and like a sponge you have been soaking up everything that has been given to you. The time is coming now when you might consider squeezing the sponge a bit and deluging the youngsters in the Troop with some of your wisdom.

Do not wait until you are asked to help. Offer to lend a hand in the group just as you are doing at home, and the offer will mean as much to your Scouters as any benefit which they may derive from the actual help you give.

You can cut out any of the "padding for odd moments" to fit this in, but do not disturb the first five priorities on any account.

You may have heard your Scouters talking lately about leakage in the Boy Scout Group, and indeed the loss of so many boys who do not complete the journey from Cub to Rover is worrying some of us older folk. There is a tremendous leak amounting almost to a burst between the Pack and the Troop which must be closed somehow, and yet another between the Troop and the Senior Troop due to the lack of good Senior Scouters. You have survived both these danger spots, and when the Queen's Scout Badge is safely on your arm, you can look forward to enjoying many more years of happy Scouting.

The Rover Crew is a very good thing when service to others inspires its every action, or a completely useless thing if it sits on its haunches and waits to be entertained at Moots and Conferences.

But for the best of you there is only one way to repay the rent you owe for your room on earth, and that is by becoming a pathfinder and taking out a Warrant as a Scouter.

It may seem a far cry now in the midst of your Senior Scouting to imagine yourself running a Troop or Pack, but it seemed a far cry when you were a Wolf Cub to imagine yourself a Senior Scout. Surely it is from the ranks of its First Class Senior Scouts that the Movement must look for its future leaders.

So when I see a Senior Scout disappearing, I feel like the monk in Bernard Shaw's play "St. Joan," who, on his return from the blazing stake in the market-place at Rouen, was asked by the Inquisitors if it was all over, and replied:

"I DO NOT KNOW. IT MAY BE ONLY JUST BEGINNING."

Chapter 8

THE
DUKE OF EDINBURGHS
AWARD

"HOW can I enter for the Duke of Edinburgh's Award?" is a question which Scouts and Senior Scouts are asking in increasing numbers. In a book for Senior Scouts it is reasonable to expect that question answered, and in this short chapter that expectation is realised.

The Scout Movement is known officially as an Operating Authority, which simply means that members of the Movement can gain the various awards offered in the Award Scheme. Friends of yours who are members of other organisations which are also Operating Authorities, may gain the Awards through their own organisations. For you, however, there is an advantage in that our system of badges fits into the scheme in such a way that it is possible for you to gain the Award by simply making progress in your own Scout training.

But we are running ahead of ourselves. What are these Awards and how can you get them? The Award Scheme consists of three Series of tests known as the Bronze Standard, the Silver Standard and the Gold Standard. Each of these series is divided into four sections, and to qualify for any standard you

71

have to reach a certain proficiency in *all* of the four sections. These sections, which are common to all three standards, are:—

A. Rescue and Public Service Training.
B. The Expedition.
C. Pursuits and Projects.
D. Fitness.

For those of you who decided to enter for the Award through the Scout Movement there are two qualifications which are essential before you begin. You must be at least 15 years of age (and not over 18), and secondly you must hold the First Class badge. When both these requirements have been fulfilled, you can enter by sending 2/6d. to the Training Secretary at Imperial Headquarters. You will then receive by return your Duke of Edinburgh's **Award Record** Book. This Book is your personal property and in it is carefully recorded your progress on the way to the Gold Standard of the Award.

Opening the Record Book, you will find that Scouts are excused the First Series of tests, and after your Scouter and District Commissioner have signed to the effect that you have your First Class badge, you can get straight on with passing the requirements for the Silver Standard. What do you have to do?

For Section A (*Rescue and Public Service Training*) you must gain the Ambulance badge, the Fireman badge or the Public Health badge. No doubt you have spotted that these are Public Service badges, so in qualifying for this Section you will also be advancing towards your Queen's Scout badge at the same time.

To qualify in Section B (*The Expedition*) you have to gain the Hiker badge. There is no alternative to this,

72

and who wants one when it is such a worthwhile badge to achieve? Again you will be on your way to the Queen's Scout badge, for the Hiker badge helps you towards Bushman's Thong or the Airman's badge.

Section C (*Pursuits and Projects*) provides you with a large choice. Almost any one of the Over 15 proficiency badges will earn you qualification. There are some exceptions, but these are clearly listed in your Record Book. If you choose a badge which advances you on the path to Airman's badge, Seaman's badge or the Bushman's Thong, or a Public Service badge, then again your progress in the Award will be matched with progress towards the Queen's Scout badge.

Section D, the *Fitness* Section, is passed by gaining the Senior Athlete badge. No matter what your age, you need only achieve the standards for those under 16 years of age, so far as the Award is concerned.

When all that is done, and provided you are still under 18 years of age, you will have qualified for the Silver Standard and not only that but you will have travelled part of the way to your Queen's Scout badge. For those reaching this standard there is a certificate bearing the facsimile signature of Prince Philip, and a lapel badge. You are also allowed to wear a special cloth badge on your Scout uniform. The certificate and badges will probably be presented to you on some suitable occasion in your own locality.

The Award does not end there. For now the next goal is the Gold Standard, for which you have until your 19th birthday to gain. It is quite possible that you will finish this stage in the Rover Crew or even as a Scouter. Let us look at what has to be done.

Section A at this level is in two parts. To qualify in

Part 1 you have to undergo some form of Rescue and Public Service Training. This can be a P.L.(S) Training  Course or a Cub Instructor Course. You may decide to gain the Adult Certificate of the British Red Cross Society as one of a number of possibilities, all of which are listed in the Movement's own Handbook on the Award. This Handbook can be purchased from the Scout Shops or it may be that your Scouter will already have one available for your use.

In Part 2 of Section A you have to undertake some form of service to other people for a period of 6 months. You should aim to use the knowledge gained in Part 1— for instance, if you took a Cub Instructor Course, then your service ought to be as an instructor in the Pack. Again, all the possibilities are listed in the Handbook.

For Section B at the Gold level there is no alternative so far as actual badges are concerned. The only qualification is the Senior Explorer badge—a badge to challenge any Senior Scout worthy of the name. The badge itself allows you some choice, for you can undertake your expedition on foot, by boat, cycle or on horseback.

Section C allows you once more a choice of any one Over 15 badge, with the exceptions applying once again. It is also worth reminding you that this Section can be gained on your way to the Queen's Scout badge, provided you carefully select your badge.

The Fitness Section, or Section D as it is called, requires you to achieve the standard laid down for those over 16 years who attempt the Senior Athlete badge.

When all four Sections are passed, you are entitled to receive the Gold Standard Certificate and lapel badge. These are normally presented by Prince Philip himself at special receptions held for the purpose. You will probably have read about these in the newspapers. Already Scouts

74

in uniform have attended these receptions. Will you follow their footsteps? As at the Silver Standard, there is a cloth badge available for wear on your uniform.

That, then, is the scheme by which Senior Scouts can gain the Award. For full details you must get hold of a copy of the Handbook. This will tell you where to wear your cloth badge, and other matters of interest to you. It also contains a message from Prince Philip, and from Sir John Hunt, the famed Secretary of the Award Scheme. As a fitting end to this chapter I quote from Prince Philip's message:—

"I hope that all those who take part in this scheme will find an added purpose and pleasure in their lives, and that sense of satisfaction which comes from successfully overcoming a challenge or helping others to overcome it.

PHILIP."

Part 2

THE OPEN AIR

Chapter 9

CAMPING AND HIKING

T HE first thing to be said is that, as Scouts, we have inherited a camping tradition which somehow or other has got to be maintained. To live on the reputation of one's forbears is about the most demoralising thing that can happen to anyone—to a nation, a family, a school, or a Troop; and let no one imagine that it cannot happen to *us*.

What sort of reputation have we got?

The evidence shall speak for itself.

In the post-war years, camping, which in earlier days had been rather a specialised activity, became so immensely popular with the *hoi polloi* that the need for some sort of control became quite evident. In 1947 the Government of the day brought in "The Control of Camping Order" which laid down certain restrictions on the use of agricultural land for camping purposes and gave power to Local Authorities to introduce their own bye-laws on the subject. But—this is the point—of the many organisations which included camping among their key activities, only two were specifically exempted from the provisions of the Act; and of these we were one.

Obviously, in the opinion of the highest authority in the land, we, at any rate, could be trusted to camp in a reasonable manner. Such was our reputation.

"Now, about the Scouts," one can imagine the Minister of the Department concerned saying to the Under-Secretary, "I take it they come in rather a different category, what? Know their stuff, don't they? Been at it a long time. Got it all at their fingertips—latrines, food storage, refuse disposal—all that."

"Yes, sir," the Under-Secretary would reply. "There's no doubt they take a great pride in what they call their 'Camping Standard.' Anybody who lets the side down gets a rocket from the rest. In addition to which, of course, the Scout Movement has its own internal system of control and inspection. It works admirably, too, I believe. Keeps 'em all on their toes."

And so on.

A bit fanciful, this imaginary conversation in Whitehall, you think? Not at all. It might have happened just like that.

Anyhow, the fact remains that today farmers and landowners can allow members of our Movement to camp on

"*The blue-eyed boys.*"

their property without having to go through all the rigmarole that would be necessary in other cases. We, in fact, when it comes to camping, are the blue-eyed boys. Blame the Scouts of yesteryear for that! Blame them for their good behaviour in the countryside, their high standards of hygiene and cleanliness, their scrupulous attention to detail. They it was who established the tradition. Ours is the responsibility for maintaining it.

It's a nuisance in a way, if you care to look at it like that. So much easier not to bother! There is always a handy clump of nettles into which you can throw your empty tins. Why bother to burn-bash-bury? . . . You don't *have* to wash on a cold, wet morning. Who's to know? . . . And if your cooking fire *does* scorch the turf a bit round the edges, no one will notice that in the lonely spot you've chosen as your camp-site. . . . The devil's advocate is never very far from your ear at moments like this, and he always clinches his argument in the same convincing way: what's it matter for once?

What's it matter?

A discarded bus-ticket, a screwed-up paper bag, the fag-end of a sausage roll . . . and on the day after August

Bank Holiday litter by the ton is removed from the royal parks of London Town, and we are known to the world, and deserve to be known, as a nation of litter-louts.

A wet towel lying on a groundsheet. An axe "masked" in a growing tree. Soapsuds in the horse-trough. Potato-peelings and porridge on the sandy bottom of the river. A gate left swinging in the wind. . . .

What's it matter?

Answer that one for yourself.

*   *   *

"Soapsuds in the horse-trough."

No attempt will be made in this chapter to instruct you in the technique of campcraft. That is something you will have learned the hard way as a Boy Scout. Discomfort is a great convincer. By practical experience, no doubt, you have discovered that what it says in the book-of-the-words is true:—

> that the cold *does* strike upwards at night, so that it pays to have plenty of insulation between you and the ground;
>
> that guy-ropes *do* need slackening before you turn in;
>
> that you *do* wake up with a head if you've slept in a hermetically-sealed tent;
>
> that stew *does* taste better if cooked on a slow fire;
>
> that split wood *does* burn best;
>
> that clay *is* non-absorbent;
>
> that wasps *do* find their way unerringly into the un-covered jam-pot;
>
> . . . and so on.

You could amuse yourself some wet day in camp by compiling your own list of the snippets of camping lore which you have collected like marbles throughout your Scouting career, and you will probably be astonished by the wealth of knowledge you didn't know you possessed!

Do not, however, be content with your small-boy

winnings. As you grow towards manhood your angle on Scouting will certainly change. You've got to be your age.

If you refer to your list of "snippets" you will probably find that ninety per cent of them have to do with your own comfort and safety in camp, or at most with the well-being of your own Patrol.

Perhaps the time has come when you should look wider in your search for camping knowledge and experience.

"Finding a new camp site."

How, for instance, would you set about finding a new camp site for your Patrol or Troop? Who would you approach for help and advice other than your own Scouters? What are the essential features you would go for in the selection of a site?

Wood. Water. Accessibility. Protection (from the elements, from pests of all kinds, human and otherwise). Outlook. Food supplies (menus and quantities). Medical and other services. Lines of communication. Sanitation. Refuse disposal. Bathing. Boating. Scope for expeditions and adventure. Under each of these headings there are a number of guiding principles which are the adult equivalent of the "snippets" of your Boy Scout days. You might do worse than set out to master them, and then—as you did as a Boy Scout— put them to practical application.

To put it another way: no longer should you rely on your Scouter to do all the thinking for you. Good camps don't just happen. They are planned. As a keen young P.L. you no doubt imagined that when you'd supervised the erection of your Patrol tent, set up your camp kitchen, cooked your own supper, and successfully persuaded the chaps to pipe down and go to sleep, you had pretty well brought the whole thing off as a solo effort—with, of course, a limited amount of help from your Second. Skip, you probably thought, hadn't needed to do a thing.

Well, that's all right. It does you no harm when you are young to feel that you're standing on your own feet.

But *you* know, and I know, that in those days Skip did far more backstage work than you realised at the time. It is this backstage stuff that now presents itself as your new field of operations.

A bit dull, you think, compared with "wood-smoke at twilight," and all that goes with it?

Well, it's different, certainly, but I'd hardly call it dull. It's a new angle, a new line of approach; and, after all, that is what you are looking for. You may regret the passing of the enchantment of your early camps, when you were just spirited away from home by those Olympian creatures, your Scouters, to find yourself in the green wonderland of an unfamiliar countryside; but that's life for you! The novelty wears thin, the magic begins to evaporate. The word "camp" which once evoked delicious small-boy visions of dark pine trees against the sky, the sparkle of dew-drenched grass in the early morning, the distant bark of a dog-fox at night—that word now has a different meaning. How to get the heavy equipment from the railhead to the site? Who's going to find out about the time of the early services at the Parish Church (and what about the two R.C. boys in the Peckers?). Where shall we put the "lats" so that they're reasonably screened by the trees without being inaccessible after dark? Somebody's got to think ahead. It had better be you.

The Camp Warden Badge will give you your immediate target, if you haven't already qualified. Even if you have, there is still plenty to learn.

* * * *

Come to think of it, the one unique feature of Scout camping which has not been cribbed or copied is the ubiquitous camp gadget. To the normal Scout, a gadgetless camp would be unthinkable. Other (non-Scout) campers never seem to use 'em. By custom and usage the copyright remains firmly in our hands.

Now the classic definition of a gadget is: "Anything useful made from materials found on the spot." But the truth is that we love the things for their own sake. Keen

83

young Tenderfeet spend hours making camp dressers which shed a cataract of pots and pans every time you look at them. At the entrance to every Patrol kitchen there is an elaborate self-closing gate which no one ever uses because it is so much easier to step over the sisal fence-rail! We have boot-scrapers that never scrape a boot, and shoe-racks that are for ever empty. But the P.L. of the Bulldog Patrol would consider himself a poor mortal indeed if his Patrol camp were not fully equipped with such aids to comfort and convenience.

That is all very well for the *Boy* Scout. Nobody minds a bit if *his* gadgets are more amusing than utilitarian, or if they conform to a fairly rigid convention. But I want to suggest that if gadget-making is to remain an activity for Senior Scouts, it must develop beyond the primitive stage of the mug-tree and the plate-rack, and stock lines of that sort.

I once had the task of showing a high official of the Ministry of Education round a national Jamboree camp. The day was hot, the way was long, and my companion seemed completely apathetic. In vain I drew his attention to the many interesting examples of rustic architecture in the camp kitchens through which we wended our dusty way. That M.O.E. official gave the impression of one who could not care less.

Then we came upon a scene of great animation. A bunch of Senior Scouts had rigged up a patent gadget of their own—a sort of super shower-bath, consisting of a short, steep run-way, up which was hauled at great speed a snatch-block with a large galvanised dustbin of water suspended from it. When the block reached the head of the run, a trip-wire came into operation to upset the bin, and the contents were precipitated with terrific force on to the cluster of bathers below.

"Very sensible."

"Very sensible, very sensible indeed,"

murmured my companion, mopping his streaming brow. "And that's what you call a gadget, is it?"

"Er—yes, sir," I said.

He nodded. "Very sensible," he said again, and we moved on.

The sight seemed to cheer him up enormously, and from that moment the tour was an undoubted success.

It was his use of the word "sensible" that interested me. What had impressed him was not that the Senior Scouts were having a lot of fun (which was undoubtedly the *raison d'être* of their enterprise), but that they had improvised something from the materials available to meet what, in the sober judgment of that over-heated government official, was a very real need at the moment—the need to cool off. It was, in fact, the *immediacy* of the device that appealed to him.

He was right, too.

During the War the Anglo-Saxon genius for improvisation revealed itself in striking fashion in the prison camps of Germany and the Far East. For further details, read or re-read the classic "escape" stories of the period. How far Scout training contributed to the success of the many strange and remarkable gimmicks that were designed in those places to facilitate escape or to make life more tolerable is a matter for conjecture, but certainly in the face of such evidence no one can say that gadget-making is "kid's stuff."

Have you ever tried weaving your own straw-mattress or windbreak on a camp loom? What about making and operating a bodger's lathe? Or a Fiji oven? Or a camp "fridge" operated by the natural processes of evaporation?

A water-filter that really worked would make a nice change, would it not? You might like to try that. Or an incinerator guaranteed to consume anything combustible. Don't ask me how. The idea would be for you to experiment and find out. There is always room for development and research. Only in this way will gadget-making be kept alive as an activity for Senior Scouts. After all, somebody has got to keep breaking new ground. Who better than yourself?

*   *   *   *

Finally, on the subject of camping in general, let it be said that mastery of the technique is only an introduction to adventure, not by any means the whole of it.

In your early days you were no doubt preoccupied with the novelty of fending for yourself, and found plenty to interest you in the camp itself and its immediate surroundings. Now that you can more or less take all that in your stride, you must certainly "look wider." What you do in camp is of vital importance. Now is the time to build that bridge, to explore that ravine, to delve into the life of the nearby village. Who knows but that the leader of the local bellringers would not be only too glad to give you your first lesson?—or the village craftsman an introduction to his craft? You could spend a whole day surveying a square half-mile of country, a night in a tree-top shelter, on a raft in the mere, or tramping towards the point on the skyline where you reckon the sun must rise at his appointed time. You live in an island teeming with interest. Camp brings your eye to the lens. The rest is up to you.

*   *   *   *

Hiking—the mobile camp—is undoubtedly the ideal all-the-year-round activity for Senior Scouts. It may be that there are bigger and better thrills to be had rock-climbing, caving, or boating, or in some such specialist activities, and one can imagine that the exponents of those virile sports would regard with modified rapture the delights of shouldering thirty pounds of kit across rough ground on a sweltering August day. On the other hand, not everyone sees much future in being scared stiff on the end of a climbing-rope, or sitting on a damp thwart for hours on end waiting for a puff of wind. Every man to his sport; and there can be no doubt that by far the majority of us plump for hiking.

What are the ingredients of a good hike?

I would put companionship first.

It is difficult to see why, but some- how you never forget the man you have hiked with. You may forget the incidents of the journey, where you camped, the meals you enjoyed, the places you visited, but the chaps who shared your joys and sorrows—these you will never forget.

"Companionship first!"

Scouters who have lived together throughout a Wood Badge Course in the close fellowship of a Scout Patrol have told me that it was not until the hike at the end of the week that they really got to know and appreciate each other fully. And I believe this to be true. There is something in the act of tramping along together that generates the very spirit of friendship. And in our Movement, as you know, we place the highest value on just that.

Next, adventure.

Adventure, we are told, lies just off the beaten track.

Let me tell you of an adventure I missed. I shall always regret it.

I was sitting in a teashop in Newcastle upon Tyne one dismal Saturday evening some years ago after a very wet and sticky game of "rugger" at Gosforth Park. Outside the rain was drenching down, and a mournful westerly wind was sweeping down the valley of the Tyne.

The teashop was crowded with weekend shoppers, and the air was bright with chatter and the merry clinking of teacups.

A hand fell on my shoulder, and I looked up to find my friend, "Vagabond," of the *Newcastle Evening Chronicle* towering above me. He was hatless as usual, and, as usual, carried a rucksack on his shoulder.

"Come on," he said, "I'll take you up the Tarretburn and over the top into Redewater."

He meant it, too.

Of course, I didn't go. "Vagabond" went off alone—as he did almost every weekend, winter and summer throughout the year—and on the following Friday I read all about it in his weekly "open-air" article in the local paper.

Nothing much had happened to him. No sensational "adventures." Just a steady, satisfying sort of *adventure*, without the quotes. He had pitched camp on that Saturday night above the snowline on the banks of the Tarretburn near Tarset, and had wakened in the small hours to visit an otter slide nearby. The otters had failed to appear, but he had seen a dog-fox trotting homeward with a chicken in his mouth, and—rare spectacle—a stoat in his winter-white diving into a pool in pursuit of a trout.

On the following day he'd called by arrangement on his friend the blacksmith at Greenhaugh, or some such place, to collect a couple of shire horses which had been left for shoeing, and had taken them over the brae-tops to Redewater. After tea at the farm he'd caught the Newcastle-bound bus from Jedburgh and reached home in time for supper and bed.

I shall always regret that lost opportunity. At the time, "Vagabond's" invitation had seemed the height, or depth, of absurdity. To accept it would have been madness—then. But how I wish I had it—now!

Adventure comes by accident. You cannot manufacture it. But you *can* put yourself in its way, and in your choice of route, in the timing of your hike, in keeping your

"Adventure comes by accident."

eyes open and your ear to the ground, you can greatly increase the *probability* of adventure. After all, Senior Scouting is an activity for intelligent people. . . .

Third among the ingredients of good hiking I put—purpose.

The glory of the hike lies in the journey itself, in the very act of wayfaring; in observing as you go; in the small-change of incident and interest that every mile contributes. But you will find that your appreciation of all these things is sharpened if you have in mind a definite objective.

In the example of the lost adventure quoted above, my friend "Vagabond" had two things in mind: to watch the otters at sport, and to do a good turn to the Redewater farmer. On another occasion, as I well remember, he went off to inspect and report on the ravages of a forest fire in Keilder Forest, on another merely to watch the sunrise from the crown of Cheviot on Midsummer Day. In every case the theme of his journey was simply a peg **on** which to hang his weekly article. You might do worse than to adopt the same technique—be clear about the peg, and the rest will follow.

In my own Rover Squire days one of our most successful efforts was a winter visit to Dunstanburgh Castle to test the accuracy of a statement in a book called "Highways and Byways in Northumberland" that at certain states of the tide with a nor'-easterly wind a-blowing, the celebrated "Rumble Churn"—a deep pothole in the massive Gull Crag on which stood the castle—would sometimes spout like an arctic whale. This entailed a grim night in the ruins and an early rise at three a.m. to catch the tide. Result: *nil*. But we saw something even more thrilling—the billowing curtains of the Northern Lights over the sea. An unforgettable sight.

As this chapter comes to an end, we hear of an attempt by a party of Senior Scouts from Kent to follow the line of the Scottish Border without deviation from coast to coast. They have found their peg. Their adventure is assured. Go you and do likewise.

Chapter 10

EXPEDITIONS WITH TRIKE-CARTS

WE were planning the route for our Senior Troop Expedition. Incautiously I remarked, "I don't know whether you will get the carts along that particular stretch; it's very rough country." Immediately, as if taking up a challenge, my Patrol Leaders said, "But the trike-carts will go anywhere!" Recognising a quotation from my own words, I hastily climbed down, and the planning continued.

"Trike-carts will go anywhere."

But, before talking about carts and kit, let me explain why we were planning a mobile expedition, and why I recommend it to you. If you have been a Scout for three or four years, you should be experienced in general campcraft: that is, you should be able—in all weathers—to pitch and strike your tent, to cook your food and maintain a clean site, to keep yourself healthy and your reserve kit dry, and above all to remain cheerful whatever happens. Now you are ready to use this experience as a means to larger exploration and adventure, in the spirit of the Senior Scout motto.

Such an opportunity is given by the moving expedition, covering a wide tract of country, usually remote and mountainous. The fact that such country nearly always has a high rainfall is just one of the hazards of the game. Here are natural obstacles to be overcome, and problems of transport to be solved: routes must be found, and camping gear taken over swollen rivers and bare passes.

Horizons are ever changing, and each day brings its rewards: the surprise view of mountain and sea, a splendid sunset, or just a hot meal after a hard day. Through it all there is the joy of companionship and endeavour in the friendly circle of the Senior Troop. Some of your happiest and most rewarding memories of Scouting will be recalled by the words "on trek."

If you decide on such an expedition, you appear to have a choice of two methods, each of which has some disadvantages. First you can hike, taking everything in or on rucsacs; in which case you will be free to go anywhere. This is probably the best method if there are only two or three in the party, if the greater part of the route is over completely trackless country, or if you are going for only a few days. But for ten or fifteen days your complete kit will be of such a weight that you can rarely forget that it is on your shoulders. Cooking gear for the Senior Patrol or Troop does not pack very conveniently in rucsacs, and the quartermaster has a considerable problem when his stores have to be collected from a dozen or more rucsacs every evening.

Second, there is the trek-cart of the familiar two-wheeled variety. This is an asset to a Group, especially for getting Patrol equipment to a nearby weekend camp. For a Senior Expedition it would solve the weight problem, but it would also limit the route to roads, or to tracks of fair width and surface—a serious disadvantage, especially in mountainous country. Such a cart must also be dismantled if the Troop travels by train to the starting point.

Fortunately, there is a third possibility, which provides a successful compromise between the other two. This is the trike-cart, a small one-wheeled cart in which the load is supported directly above the wheel (as in the Chinese wheelbarrow, I believe). One man steers the cart from behind by means of two shafts, and motive power is supplied, when required, by two drag-ropes attached to the centre of the front, and pulled by two, four, or six chaps, according to the gradient and surface encountered.

On the level, the drag-ropes can be detached, and going

downhill the steersman can have the pleasure of "gallumphing"— a combination of running and floating through the air peculiar to trekking with the trike-cart!

This vehicle meets the previous criticisms of the other schemes. It will go practically anywhere; certainly over any path, however narrow. Though it is at its best on tracks or footpaths, it can be pulled for short distances over mountain passes or moorland.

"Gallumphing."

Trike-carts have crossed the Lairig Ghru in the Cairngorms and Sty Head in the Lake District, and have negotiated Urra Moor, the summit ridge of the Cleveland Hills. Such crossings require time and hard work, but compensation comes again on the level. A simple adjustment to the shafts enables the cart to be lifted bodily over walls, and to be carried stretcherwise through bogs and rivers. Ultimately, if the going becomes too rough for even this to be practicable, the cart is light enough to be dismantled and distributed, with its load, among the members of the expedition. On rail journeys a loaded trike-cart is accepted as personal luggage, and it goes bodily into a guard's van without any difficulty.

But the most important advantages of trike-carts are less tangible ones. First, with all tentage, groundsheets, bedding, cooking gear, and food on carts, the weight of your rucsac, containing only clothing and other personal kit, can be reduced until you are hardly conscious of it. Second, the work of pulling the cart, when necessary, can be shared between older and younger members of the Patrol according to their capacity. Third, and most important, the cart keeps the Patrol together as a team, providing a focal point for the day's activity, and preventing the straggling that is liable to occur when hiking. "Getting the cart through" is actually a challenge in itself. It sounds irrational; but then so are many other adventurous activities.

When strangers first hear of the trike-cart, they say, "It's impossible: you can't balance it!" If you feel like saying this, I can only reply that we *can* and we *have done* on several expeditions and over hundreds of miles. The steering and balance can be mastered in a matter of hours, and an expert can keep the cart upright under practically any conditions. It is as easy as learning to ride a bicycle— or easier, for at least you have your feet on the ground —and it depends on exactly the same principle: you steer the cart towards the side to which it leans. The cart can be parked by tilting it forward so that it rests on the wheel and the front ends of the shafts.

The trike-cart already has a considerable history, having been originated in the 1920's by Dr. G. F. Morton, then Headmaster of Leeds Modern School, who used the carts on magnificent treks with his Scouts in Scotland, the Alps, the Cevennes, and the Rocky Mountains. He describes these expeditions in his two books, *Hike and Trek* and *Hike and Hero,* which are now unfortunately out of print, but which may be found in some Scout Group libraries. Since then several Groups have constructed their own trike-carts, but they have never been mass-produced. Construction depends to a considerable extent on getting the help of a friendly engineering firm with facilities for welding and brazing.

The diagrams show the main lines of the design. The frame measures 33 in. by 20 in., and is made of angle-steel welded at the corners. The 16-in. wheel, supplied complete by Dunlop, runs on ball-bearings and has an industrial cushion (i.e. solid) tyre. A pneumatic tyre is

Scale: 1/30

93

possible, and would be lighter; but it would necessitate carrying a repair outfit and a foot pump. The whole cart weighs only 60 lb., and will carry a load of anything from 100 lb. to 150 lb.

A full description and pictures of a recent model of trike-cart appeared in *The Scouter* for January, 1955. Scale drawings of this model, blueprints of which cost 2s. 6d., can be obtained from the Maidstone Grammar School Scout Group. We do not say it is the last word, and other Senior Troops will no doubt enjoy devising their own modifications; but the main lines have been proved to be successful.

The trike-cart can be used for either Troop or Patrol expeditions. With a Senior Troop of three Patrols we take three carts, each the responsibility of a Patrol. The first carries all the tents and groundsheets, contained in a large canvas bag; the second takes the sleeping-bags, similarly enclosed. The third cart carries a light box, with a canvas cover, which contains cooking gear and food supplies. If a Senior Patrol goes off on its own with one cart, this box, which has three separate sections, will contain food, cooking gear, and bedding, while the tents are roped on outside. The box also acts as a larder in camp.

EQUIPMENT

I must emphasise at the outset that although the trike-carts ease the weight problem, they do not give you *carte blanche* to take vast quantities of heavy equipment. We have had 200 lb. on a cart, but it becomes very difficult to manage then; so the load should if possible be kept down to 100 lb. per cart. You must therefore make all equipment as light as possible.

TROOP EQUIPMENT

1. *Tentage* should be of waterproof and rotproof Egyptian cotton cloth. It is possible to make a tent large enough to sleep a whole Patrol, but you may have difficulty in finding a flat piece of ground large enough to pitch it, and in rough weather it will offer a big area to the wind. It is therefore better to go in for hike-tents

94

housing two or three Scouts each. If you choose the conventional two-pole design, get it with an apse end, which conveniently houses rucsacs. But we prefer single-pole tents, which give greater floor-space and head-room for the same weight (about 5 lb.), and sleep three Seniors comfortably. In either case, I recommend you to add flysheets as soon as you can afford them. You probably would not take them if you were hiking, but with the trike-carts the extra weight (2¾ lb.) is well worth while. Your routes are likely to be in rainy localities; with a flysheet you can move about comfortably in the tent and be absolutely watertight (provided you have chosen your site sensibly). In addition, you may have to strike and fold your tent in a downpour and pitch it again that evening under the same conditions: you can do this *under* a flysheet without getting the tent itself wet at all.

2. A *groundsheet* which fits the tent and pegs down is a pleasant luxury, but is always more expensive than two of the 6 ft. by 3 ft. sheets which most Seniors possess in any case; so this item may well be left for individuals to provide.

3. When buying *cooking gear* get aluminium ware; it is worth the extra expense. Each Patrol can do with a nest of three dixies, and a frying-pan, with which they can cook a meal for themselves on their own fire. We find such Patrol cooking best on trek; but an occasional alternative is to get each Patrol to cook one course for the whole Troop: thus, one Patrol could produce the porridge (always welcome, morning and evening, on trek), the second could fry something, while the third brewed tea or cocoa. For carrying dixies, make strong plastic bags, which are soot-proof as well as waterproof: you probably won't want to clean the outsides of your dixies every morning, though it is as well to do so at the end of each trek. Another such bag can hold oddments—bread-knife, ladle, etc.—which take but little space. On top of the food-cart you can carry one or more bowls; they make washing and washing-up more con-

venient if you are not able to camp by a river or lake.

4. *Miscellaneous items* will include a Troop first-aid box, an oilcan for the carts, and some trowels for fireplaces and sanitary purposes. Latrine screens are not necessary if your route is a sensible one for trekking. An axe is an optional extra; personally, I consider that you can always get a large enough fire with wood you can break under your foot.

PERSONAL EQUIPMENT

1. It is essential for each Scout to have a waterproof *rucsac*, preferably with a frame. It need not be large or heavy, but plenty of pockets make orderly packing easier. The models which enable the load to be carried high on the shoulders are recommended for comfort. The contents will not include bedding or a groundsheet, but must nevertheless be rigorously limited in weight, say, to 12 lb., for the sake both of the individual and of the team. It is no fun pulling a trike-cart *and* carrying a heavy rucsac.

2. *Bedding* must also be light and compact. A down or feather-down sleeping-bag is ideal, and you can buy all the materials for making one. Some ready-made ones can be improved by incorporating a zip-fastener. It is false economy to buy kapok-filled bags: they are heavy and bulky, and go lumpy in time. If you have blankets, sew them into a bag and roll them up. Whatever your bedding, it should be in an individual plastic bag to ensure that it keeps really dry. Though the canvas bag on the cart is waterproof, it may have to be packed or unpacked in pouring rain.

3. *Footwear* must be decided on many months ahead. Your shoes or boots must be sound, but must have been broken in by plenty of long walks before the trek begins. Ankle socks reduce friction. Harden your feet by walking, and by rubbing with methylated spirits or with one per cent formalin for several weeks. On trek, use boric acid powder daily.

4. *Rainwear* must be waterproof and ventilated. Mackintoshes and similar sealed garments may result in your getting soaked with perspiration. Cycle-capes

are awkward when you are hauling on a cart-rope. An anorak is excellent for general use, but will not keep out continuous heavy rain. You can supplement it with a small home-made plastic cape to cover your rucsac and shoulders at the points where rubbing may cause leakage.

5. Personal *first-aid kit* should include (*a*) boric acid powder, animal wool, chiropodists' felt and elastoplast, for foot care; (*b*) an insect repellant, of the dimethylphthalate variety; and (*c*) sunburn protection, especially if you are going on high or snow-covered mountains.

PLANNING A SUMMER TREK

You will be wise to settle your dates and choice of route, of which I shall say more later, by February or March. Do not attempt to cover too great a distance: an average of ten miles a day is enough and provides plenty of variety. You should trek for three days, say, and then spend one or two days at a "rest-camp." From this you may climb a peak, or hike to the sea; but it will be a change and so will fit you for the next three days' trekking.

Unless your party is very large, it is hardly necessary to fix up your one-night camp sites in advance. Indeed, Dr. G. F. Morton insisted that part of the adventure of trekking was *not* knowing where you would sleep. The leader will, however, be glad to know of possible camp sites along the route, through having either studied the map or consulted local Scouters beforehand. Permission may be needed to cross or camp on private estates. The rest-camps should usually be fixed up in advance, because if you are in remote country you will probably have to have your food supplies delivered to them by some means. In the Highlands this may be by boat.

"Not knowing where you are going to sleep."

You will find that you can carry two days' food on the carts fairly comfortably. If you want to be independent of civilisation for longer, experiment with hard-ration packs.

The railway authorities, who like ample warning of party travel, should be contacted about May. British Railways give useful reductions to Scout parties, and Seniors under sixteen travel at half the fare for those over sixteen. You can travel out to one station and back from another and still get the reduction. Your equipment, including the trike-carts themselves, should come well within the free luggage allowance, which is 56 lb. under sixteen and 112 lb. over sixteen.

Every member of the party should be an experienced camper, so that he can do his full share in camp without further instruction. But during the summer you should have a practice trek for a weekend over the hardest route you can find in your neighbourhood. This gives the Patrols an opportunity of working out their trek routine, and shows up weaknesses in feet, and elsewhere, in time to remedy them.

Choice of District and Route

The ideal area for a trek of the kind I have in mind is one in which you can go for long distances on footpaths or minor tracks. You can include short stretches over passes or moors without paths, recognising that they will involve hard work and that therefore you will do a shorter mileage on that day. You will, of course, avoid motor roads and large centres of population (except perhaps at the end of a trek, when a "slap-up" meal is a legitimate extravagance).

There is no doubt that the best routes in Great Britain are to be found in *Scotland*. There I suggest:

1. Two routes from Strath Glass, south-west of Inverness, over to and along the West Coast—

(*a*) By Glen Affric over to the head of Loch Duich; then follow the wonderful coast southward to Glenelg, Arnisdale, Inverie, and Morar. There are grand peaks to climb on the way, and two of Scotland's finest sealochs to cross by boat.

(b) By Glen Strathfarrar to Achnashellach and Torridon; climb Beinn Eighe and Liathach; then follow the coast southward to finish at Kyle of Lochalsh and the boat to Mallaig.

2. The coast of Ross-shire and Sutherland, from Ullapool northward. A very remote stretch of country dotted with queer mountains, such as Stac Polly and Suilven, which provide exciting climbing.

3. The Cairngorms, from Aviemore to Linn of Dee and on to Blair Atholl. The famous Lairig Ghru provides a great challenge; a somewhat easier route is the Lairig an Laioch, farther east.

4. From Dalwhinnie to Kinlochlaggan; then by General Wade's road over the Corrieairack Pass to Fort Augustus. This route can be extended to include Ben Nevis.

5. Follow the Road to the Isles "by Loch Tummel and Loch Rannoch and Lochaber to the sea." Make a detour into Glen Lyon, longest glen in Scotland, and finish either in Glen Coe or by coming down Glen Nevis from Lochtreighead.

Ireland would appear to offer promising routes:

1. In the Donegal Highlands, for striking mountains and 1,000-ft. cliffs on the coast.

2. In Kerry, among MacGillycuddy's Reeks, Ireland's highest mountains.

In *Wales,* try to trace the Roman road known as Sarn Helen from the Dovey Valley to Snowdonia, finishing with a climbing camp there.

In *England* it is more difficult to keep off the roads, but the following are possibilities:

1. A circuit of the Lake District—though this area suffers from over-popularity and resulting difficulty in finding suitable camp-sites.

2. Follow the middle section of Hadrian's Wall, from Brampton to Corbridge, combining considerable historical interest with a stiff route. Near Humshaugh, find the site of the first Scout camp.

3. The Pennine Way—230 miles, from the Derbyshire Peak to the Scottish Border—is at present largely a line

on planners' maps; but when it has been established it will be a fine trek route. The Yorkshire Dales, on its middle section, provide a great choice of routes already.

4. Follow the summit ridge of the South Downs, from Beachy Head to Chichester. A breezy route over springy turf, with views of the Weald and the Channel.

5. By the Pilgrims' Way from Winchester to Canterbury—another route rich in history.

On the *Continent* you can devise many trekking routes, but keep away from the big tourist centres. Promising areas are the Vosges, the Jura, the Cevennes, and possibly the Savoy Alps in France; the Black Forest in south-west Germany; and the fjords of Norway, which would be very fine, but expensive to reach. On some Continental railways you will have to pay a freight charge on trike-carts. If you want to get a general impression of a country, it may be better to have a number of short standing camps in different places and explore from these. In any case, you must start planning earlier, aiming to have your complete scheme in the hands of the International Secretary by April 1st at the latest.

*   *   *   *

So there you are. I have thrown out some ideas, and it is up to you to develop them. I hope that you will find as much satisfaction in trekking as we have found.

Chapter 11

CAMPING ABROAD

THERE are, as we all know, countless opportunities for a Senior Scout to find adventure in his own countryside; so much so that one sometimes hears the question asked: "Why go to all the trouble of organising a foreign camp when there is so much to be seen and done in our own country?" The answer is, of course, that there is nothing quite like a camp abroad. It is an experience, every moment of which is an adventure into something new; every step of which widens our horizons, bringing new knowledge, new friendships, wider understanding, new and exciting possibilities for the future. To all this is added, for Scouts, the fuller realisation of what the World Brotherhood really means—something which only a World Jamboree can give more fully.

You have almost certainly thought of all these things if you have ever considered camping abroad. The planning of a first camp across the water is something which brings with it an ever-increasing excitement. Yet Scouts have sometimes come home from foreign camps terribly disappointed and with a firm resolution never to go again. The purpose of this chapter is to help you to avoid such disappointment. It *can* be avoided; it *should* be avoided, and, in ninety-nine cases out of a hundred, it is the fault of the Scouts themselves if it is not avoided.

At home you know the ropes; you are familiar with the language; the customs of the people; the laws; the currency and the weights and measures. In any sort of difficulty you know just where to go and what to do. Even so, you visit your site beforehand; you plan carefully for food supplies; you get all the necessary permissions and, if you are hiking or cycling, you plan your route

"Not afraid of the unknown."

carefully and anticipate any likely snags. If you are going abroad it means that you are not afraid of the unknown—but it does not mean that the unknown can be disregarded. Planning is far more important for a camp abroad—remember that you will probably be unable to visit your site before you arrive. This is in no way said to discourage you. The planning of a foreign camp can be as interesting an occupation for the winter months as any a Senior Troop could undertake. You will be finding out something new all the time; and what you find out will be of permanent value to you and the Troop. You will be building up a fund of knowledge which, together with your own organisation, will ensure a really fine adventure which you can appreciate to the very full when once you start upon it.

The first thing to decide is, naturally, the country to which you are going. You may have heard of good camps other Troops have had in France, Luxembourg, Belgium, or any other country. On the other hand, you may feel that you would like to do some real exploring and go to somewhere outlandish and strange. Be careful here. You do need some experience—or someone with experience to help you. Don't attempt anything too ambitious until the Troop has found its feet and got over the teething troubles of foreign camping.

You can get plenty of colour and atmosphere without going too far off the beaten track, and the experience you gain in this way will be invaluable to you when you undertake something more advanced. So let's talk about a first camp abroad. Don't be afraid of distance. The

"Go somewhere outlandish."

102

cost of getting there is important; but you will find that party reductions go a long way towards cutting it down. If you start in really good time, before Christmas, for instance, you will be able to find out about all this in time to change your decision if the cost turns out to be prohibitive. On the other hand, you would have time to combine personal savings and money-making activities in such a way as to make a fairly long journey possible after all.

For a first camp abroad it is probably best to go to a place about which you already have some first-hand information. It may be impossible for you to visit the site yourself, and you should be able to obtain some reliable information about the sort of thing one would look for on a preliminary visit. You will want a foreign atmosphere, although later you may want to get right out in the wilds, and for this reason you will probably look for a place where there is a town within fairly easy reach. The ideal is, perhaps, a smallish country town with plenty of tradition, lying in surroundings which make the journey really worth while.

As soon as you have decided, write to the International Secretary at I.H.Q. and tell him what you want to do. Do this as soon as you possibly can. You will then be put on the right tracks as far as the Scouting procedure is concerned and, if you wish, put into touch with a Scouter near your proposed camp site, who will be prepared to help you. This friend abroad can be of very great service to you. He can obtain the necessary civil permissions for your camp (though it is a good and courteous thing to write yourself to the local mayor or burgomaster and ask his permission to camp in the district); he can send you the names of local tradespeople and doctors who are well disposed towards Scouts and with whom you will find it easy to deal; he can find you the nearest thing available to your ideal camp site—a regular organised site if you prefer that sort of thing, or a site where you can be alone and completely independent. It is up to you to see that his willingness to help is not turned into a burden. If you possibly can, persuade a schoolmaster or some other friend

103

to act as secretary for your planning and write to him in his own language; this will enable him to answer in his. Don't forget that postage from abroad is often more expensive than the corresponding rate from England: enclose an International Reply Coupon with each letter you send abroad which requires an answer. These coupons cost 1/- and are available at all main post offices. Don't burden him with questions to which you could easily obtain the answer; and don't expect him to do your ordering from the local tradespeople. He has his own work to do and, once you have obtained the addresses, you should do the ordering yourself.

All this, of course, applies more particularly to a standing camp, and this is almost certainly the best thing for which to plan if it is your first time overseas. This does not mean that you cannot tour. The idea is that you should treat your camp as a base from which you make a real exploration of the surrounding district. And about those explorations: don't despise your own two feet! You will get much more real adventure, much more fine scenery, much more feeling of real achievement if you get right *into* the country, than if you merely pedal along a metalled road with the Buicks, Chryslers, Peugeots and Citroëns whizzing past at fifteen-second intervals. Another thing: don't go out in hordes. The Patrol is the Scout unit, and four Seniors going off on their own for two or three nights will have a much better time and gain infinitely more in genuine Scouting experience than if they are just individuals in a crowd of twenty being pushed around the local sights by a hot and bothered Scouter. Two or three nights out; back to base for a day or two; then off again somewhere else. For this a good programme is essential. For a good exploring programme, good maps are essential. Excellent and detailed maps of all districts in the world

"Don't despise your own two feet."

can be obtained from *Sifton, Praed & Co. Ltd., 67 St. James's Street, London, S.W.1.* Your Scouter friend will be able to get you some literature from the local tourist office which will be useful when planning expeditions; but don't rely on the pretty little maps which often come with this literature. They are often most inaccurate.

Planning must, of course, include menus; and your food is necessarily associated with the question of cost. When you go abroad you can't send home for more money. You want to be well fed; but you don't want to go bankrupt before the end of the camp, and you MUST NOT—repeat MUST NOT—simply assume that prices will be much the same as in England and then find that you have not enough money to meet your bills when the time comes to return home. Your Scout correspondent may be able to put you in touch with wholesalers who will send you complete price lists and, perhaps, supply you at wholesale prices. If not, you must write to the retailers he has recommended and ask them what you want to know. Be prepared for shocks as far as some of the prices are concerned! This is the moment to start some really important propaganda with the Troop. Remind them that they are going abroad, and

"Be prepared for shocks with prices."

that foreign food is just as much a part of their experience as foreign customs and ways of speech. You will find that you will save a great deal of money and trouble by accepting this as part of your experience. Vast areas of Europe have never heard of porridge and, if they saw it, the inhabitants would probably think that it was a poultice. Most people in Europe think that we, not they, are the food lunatics of the world. You can save money and valuable time by adopting the Continental system of a light, uncooked breakfast, and by doing without tea. A good midday meal and a good supper will more than keep

105

"Doing without tea."

you going. But, whatever you decide to do, work it out beforehand and cost it. Send your tradespeople a preliminary list of your likely requirements, together with a specific order for collection on arrival. Do this in plenty of time for them to query any items which they may not understand, such as bacon (not *quite* what they mean by *jambon* or *Speck*), sausage (they have an infinite variety of these and few of them are meant for frying), cornflakes (of which they may not have heard), and so on. The costing of all this, together with your estimates for quantities, will be complicated by your unfamiliarity with foreign money, weights and measures. Conversion graphs such as those illustrated at the end of this chapter are a great help here. When calculating your available money, don't forget that the banks, both in England and abroad, charge a small commission on each transaction. For a large party this may come to a sum which really makes a difference. The simplest thing is to work to a rate of exchange rather less favourable than the one in force. You may even find that you then have a small credit balance for adding cheer to the journey home.

The planning of the actual journey is important, too. Don't forget that your return journey needs, perhaps, even more careful planning than the outward one. The London offices of the railways of the countries you are crossing or visiting will be extremely willing to help you with advice and information—they will have all the latest information about cheap rates, baggage regulations, etc., for their section of the journey—and the Continental Superintendent at Victoria Station, London, will prove a reliable and painstaking friend who will give you with great patience all the information you require and supply the actual tickets and reservations. In some cases (the French *Colonies de Vacances* tickets, for example), you can get cheaper rates by booking directly with the railway

106

companies concerned for that particular section of your route. Normally, you can do all your bookings through the Continental Superintendent at Victoria. But you must give them time, and you must read their instructions carefully. There can be few more infuriating things than to find that you have been separated from your tents simply because you did not bother to find out whether baggage regulations were the same in other countries as in England. Think out your journey in both directions and in detail, and take nothing for granted. That is the only safe rule for a successful and carefree trip.

Passports, individual or collective, must be arranged in good time through your local Ministry of Labour Office. Money is almost as essential as a passport—and you will not be able to make any arrangements for money until you have your passports. Any bank will very willingly arrange for you to have the best advice for your particular circumstances—but banks, too, require time. Time is, in fact, of the greatest importance to good planning. You cannot expect everybody to drop everything, break all sorts of regulations and attend to your particular needs, just because you have left things until the last moment.

Once you are there, or on the way, there are one or two points to remember. First, last, and all the time, remember that you are Scouts. You not only represent the country whose flag you will be wearing on your uniform: you also represent Scouting in the country which is its home. You all *want* to do the right thing—but take the trouble to find out something of local custom—and local Scout custom—as soon as you can. Many Continental Scouts, for instance, would be surprised and hurt if they saw a British Scouter—still more a Scout—smoking in the street. For many, too, the left handshake is a much more important symbol than it is for some on this side of the Channel. Remember that, once you set foot on the other side, *you* are the foreigner. A friendly smile and a real interest in local customs will win you many friends. Laughter and nudging whenever you see anything unusual, or when you hear somebody trying to help your ignorance of languages by speaking your own imperfectly, will lose you nearly as many friends whose co-operation you would value as bluster and insistence when faced with, let us say, a regulation of which you were unaware. And, talking about Courtesy, don't forget the First Scout Law either when you are passing through the Customs. You are not *entitled* to bring back *anything* which you have *acquired* abroad. That legend about opened packets and used articles is . . . just a legend. Declare everything you have and, within reason, you will not be asked to pay duty.

Most of this has been written for those who have not camped abroad before. To cover all the possibilities of foreign camps would need a whole book, and a bigger one than this. As your foreign experience increases, you will want to tour, or to seek out some exciting place far from civilisation where you can do some really advanced Scouting. This type of expedition has its own problems, its own difficulties and, don't forget, its own dangers. Such a tour or camp can be a wonderful and unforgettable experience; but you must not undertake such an adventure lightly. Many things which can be done with safety by the trained and responsible Senior Scout are a source of real danger to the tyro who is cheerfully willing to "have a bash" but whose experience comes almost entirely from books and imagination. For such an expedition you must train, and train hard. The prospect of the expedition will give a stimulus to Troop training—First Aid; Pioneering; Rescue Work; the careful study of really good maps; high *practical* standards of camping under difficult conditions; care and maintenance of gear; collection and study of information about the area you are proposing to visit; route finding; safety rules and procedure when lost —there is *plenty* of material for Troop programmes to last a year or even two. And with the expedition in view you have a definite and concrete objective for it all. The more thoroughly you train, the more carefully you plan, the better your expedition will be and, incidentally, the better you will be for having done it. So Look Wide! It is the way to get what you hoped to get from the Senior Troop.

Now, a final word about these more advanced camps. First of all, don't confuse a journey and an exploration. An exploration means an investigation of an area—and you can't investigate an area if you simply travel through it as fast as you can. Nor is there much point in calling an expedition an exploration if you go to a well-known region which is thoroughly well mapped, caters for motorised tourists and has a little shack selling souvenirs at every beauty spot. One big advantage of exploring is that the chaps can really get away from—and stay away from—the madding crowd, or the maddening crowd, if you prefer it that way. There are still places in Europe where you can spend a fortnight or three weeks without seeing another human being—and they are usually worth looking for! The best way to explore a definite area is to radiate from a base camp. Patrols can form advanced camps away from base and stay there for several days at a time before coming back for a rest and the writing up of reports. Then off they go to form another advanced camp in a different direction. It doesn't in the least matter if patrols follow one another in the same advanced camp area—especially if each Patrol has specialised in its own particular field of investigation (insects; geology; plant-life; topography, etc.). In this way a Senior Troop can make a really worthwhile study of a little-known region and bring back information which will be welcomed even by learned societies. A first rule, of course, is to decide what you are going to investigate and to train yourselves to be competent investigators. Slipshod field work and careless notes are a waste of everybody's time and a disgrace to Senior Scouting.

If your expedition is a journey, and a journey can be great fun and a tremendous adventure, you will probably not be able to avoid contact with civilisation so completely. This is especially true if you are carrying food and have to renew supplies. Opportunities for investigation will be fewer; but you will have a wider, though possibly not such a deep, experience. A journey will be all the more fun and all the bigger adventure if your route can be chosen without having to consider the wear and tear on tyres!

But whichever you choose, remember that an expedition which deserves the name is only for really trained Scouts. Your map-reading and compass work must be perfect, and if you are lucky enough to find an area which has not been mapped, you must read your *Scouting for Boys* and your *Kephart* and make quite sure that you don't get lost—and, if you do get lost, that you know exactly what to do. Your First Aid and your Transport of the Injured techniques must be as good as you can make them—just try carrying an eleven-stone Senior over six or seven miles of rough hill country: it is better to be surprised before you go than after the accident has happened! You must know what to do if an appendix suddenly becomes a matter of urgency—it is much simpler, of course, if you have persuaded a doctor to come with you. You must have the plain common sense not to go mountaineering except under expert guidance. You must know how to examine and test your water supplies—here again, a doctor is worth his weight in purifying tablets! You must be able to pitch a tent which will stand against anything —and know what to do to save your life if it doesn't. In fact, you must be the sort of young man envisaged by B.-P. After all, it all comes down to the basic principles: *Be Prepared* and *Look Wide*. And don't imagine that your S.M.(S.) will do it all for you! He won't—because he can't. This sort of expedition is a team effort: the Patrol team and the Senior Troop team. Base your training on the normal Scout programme and develop it, as Seniors should develop it, until it becomes a real and intelligently applied adult efficiency. If you do this you can go out and have the time of your lives—and come back home alive to tell the girl-friend all about it.

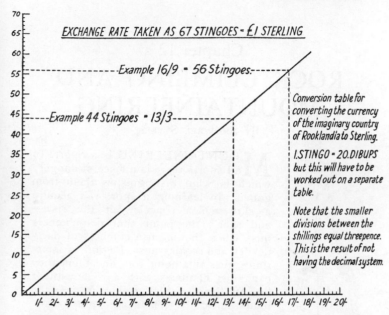

CONVERSION GRAPH.—Write out the British values along the bottom edge and the foreign values along the vertical edge, starting at the bottom left-hand corner in both cases. Make a dot at a point where an imaginary horizontal line drawn out from the foreign value meets a vertical line drawn from the corresponding British value. Join this dot to the bottom left-hand corner. By taking a horizontal line out from any foreign value until it meets this line, and then a vertical line downwards, the British equivalent can be found.

The units *une livre* and *ein Pfund* are often used by food suppliers on the Continent. They equal half a kilogramme—rather more than an English pound weight.

Chapter 12

ROCK CLIMBING AND MOUNTAINEERING

By Showell Styles

"There is a spice of danger."

MOUNTAINEERING is a Sport. In all sports there is a spice of danger, which is what distinguishes them from games. In learning a sport you acquire a skill which cancels out the risk—and that's the point that non-climbers miss when they accuse climbers of daredevilry and recklessness. Beginners sometimes miss this point too, and think they can start climbing with a rope without having learned the rudiments of the mountain craft. Then accidents occur. Before you start mountaineering you need to read all you can get hold of on the subject (a list of books is given at the end of this chapter) and have plenty of walking experience over moorlands and hill country. When you start to climb in earnest you need the proper equipment, an experienced leader, and an observant eye to note all that the leader does.

Rock Climbing is one branch of Mountain Craft. It is the most important, because the two things it needs for success—the art of Balance and the art of Using the Rope —are the basis of all mountain ascents. Snowcraft, Icecraft, Route Finding, and many other things such as the ways of glaciers and the relative trustworthiness of different kinds of rock have all to be learned before you can call yourself an all-round Mountaineer. G. Winthrop Young's book, *Mountain Craft,* sometimes called the

112

modern mountaineer's Bible, takes 140,000 words to describe the climber's art; this chapter of 3,000 words obviously cannot tell you all about mountaineering, then. What it can do is to point out the road—or set your feet in the proper holds—which will lead to your enjoyment of what many of us think is the greatest of all sports. For Senior Scouts holding the Climber Badge some of it will be in the nature of revision, but all of us need to revise our knowledge at intervals.

How to Start

Unless you are already keen on the open in general and hills in particular, it is better not to start at all. Not everyone—not even every Senior Scout—is made for a mountaineer. If you are keen, you'll already have spent some of your holidays tramping over hills and moorland, and felt the magical attraction of the peaks that lift their heads in challenge. You'll know how to find your way by map and compass in a mist and how to choose a route over rough country. You want to start mountain-climbing. Well, the best way is to begin by climbing peaks by the ordinary routes. Spend a holiday doing it, and try to make your ascents gradually harder. In North Wales, for instance, start with a fine but not difficult mountain like Moel Hebog. Next, walk the Glyder range from Capel Curig down to the Devil's Kitchen and Idwal Youth Hostel. Do a long high trek—the two Carnedds and Pen-yr-Oleu-Wen is a good one—and on these walks try a scramble or two on wayside boulders. Then ascend Tryfan by its North Ridge, down the South Ridge, and up the Bristly Ridge of Glyder Fach. Finally, tackle the Snowdon Horseshoe itself, the finest ridge-walk in England and Wales; the traverse of the "knife-edge" of Crib Goch will prove whether you have a steady head or not.

These expeditions, of course, you'll make in summer. In winter even the easiest of them may be changed to a

"Traversing the knife-edge."

113

difficult climb needing ice-axes and ropes and a high degree of skill in their use. If you have served such an apprenticeship, and want to extend your mountaincraft in the direction of Rock Climbing, you are reasonably well prepared to do so.

Never attempt to climb steep rocks with a rope unless you have a good and experienced leader on your first attempts. It takes quite a lot of experience to make a steady leader, and no matter how tough you are or how trusty your companions, you should not try it on your own. By far the best way to become a Rock Climber is to get someone who really knows his stuff to take you up a Moderate climb. (Climbs are graded Moderate, Difficult, Very Difficult, and Severe, according to their hardness.) Almost all climbers are very willing to help keen beginners and will go out of their way to show you the ropes. You may have met one during your tramps, or there may be one staying in the hostel or lodging; don't hesitate to ask him. If he sees you are really keen—and fit, and with that useful preliminary mountain-walking experience—he will be very likely to take you for a climb.

If there is no such leader to be found, the next best way is to take part in one of the mountaincraft courses which nowadays are pretty numerous in the mountain districts. Some are run from Youth Hostels, such as the frequent courses at Capel Curig Youth Hostel, and you could write for particulars of courses in other districts to the Youth Hostels Association, Welwyn Garden City, Herts. The Central Council of Physical Recreation (C.C.P.R.) has recently started mountaineering courses in several places; their address is 6 Bedford Square, London, W.C.1. Another way, and one giving a better chance of acquiring climbing skill quickly, is to hire a Certificated Mountain Guide to lead and instruct you. Both in Wales and the Lake District there are several such Guides and their charges are about £2 or £3 per day. Shared with one companion, this fee is often worth while if you are quick to learn, for in three or even two days you can do half-a-dozen good rock climbs and find your feet rapidly. The

British Mountaineering Council (Secretary), 6 Belmont Grove, Lewisham, S.E.13, will give you particulars.

Whichever method you choose for the start of your serious mountaineering, you will need to have the proper equipment *from the very first*.

EQUIPMENT

Boots are the most important item of equipment. You may have found stout nailed shoes good enough for mountain walking, but they will not do for climbing on rock, snow, or ice. If you can possibly afford good climbing-boots, made by a specialist in such matters, do save up and buy them. This applies, too, to all other mountaineering equipment. I advise writing to the following firms and asking for their catalogues:—

"Boots are most important."

Thomas Black & Son, Port Glasgow, Scotland.
Robert Lawrie Ltd., Marble Arch, London.
Camtors, 1-2 Hardwick Street, London, E.C.1.

For clothing, take a look first at the Scout Shop supplies. A look through several catalogues will enable you to compare prices and find out what you want. A pair of good nailed climbing-boots will cost you something

like £5. It is possible to make do with a pair of stout ex-Army boots—if your feet will stand them—nailed by yourself. Get "star mugger" nails, and drive them hard and true on a last as shown in the sketch. The local bootmaker will probably put them in for you more securely. But I must emphasise that this is only a very second-best, and that you will have to inspect your nails frequently for wear or needed replacement. I strongly recommend nails, clinker nails if you are getting real climbing-boots, in preference to moulded rubber soles. Rubber is delightful on dry rock, but on wet rock—in this country at least—it can be extremely treacherous.

115

For clothing you will want something rather different from the shorts and shirt and jacket that served you for hill walking. On a rock climb you can't move fast; and if there is a wind it can be very, very cold standing about on a little rock platform on a precipice, even in summer. You want *windproof* jacket and trousers to be really well outfitted. Underneath you can wear old woollen pullovers, old flannel shirt, anything warm and loose-fitting—but on top you must be windproof. An "anorak" with a hood attached is the best to get. Here, too, you can improvise a second-best, by cutting down an old raincoat to thigh length. Remember that it will have to stand rough treatment from the rocks, and that it should be capable of a good button-up to the neck. But a properly-designed windproof jacket is very much better, and also a good deal lighter; it will cost you 35s. or more.

Socks (your boots should be large enough to take two pairs), gloves, and scarf should be of wool. If you have a hooded jacket you won't need a woollen cap except outside the summer months.

Lastly, the Rope. At first, probably, your leader will provide the rope; but eventually you'll want to possess your own. There can be no second-best in this case. Your life may depend on the rope, and a bit of old clothes-line or the coil that's been hanging up in H.Q. for years simply must not be used. Save up, or club together, and buy 120 feet of Full-Weight Nylon Rope. It is expensive—£6 at the time of writing—but it will last for many years and is the best Life Insurance you can have—*when* you have learned how to use it for climbing.

CLIMBING WITH THE ROPE

Take a look at the natty diagram alongside—all my own work. It shows a "rope" of three climbers half-way up a rock climb. The dotted line represents the rope. The

Leader—Number 1—has reached a "stance" or rock platform and is "belayed" to a spike of rock above him. His belay is made by taking a loop of the rope (which is tied to his waist with a bowline) and placing it over the spike. The loop is made with an overhand knot. So Number 1, once he is up, cannot fall off or be pulled off by Number 2, who is in the act of climbing the "pitch." Number 1 is "belaying" him as he comes up, taking in the rope with his right hand; from that hand the rope passes round across his back and over his left shoulder to his left hand. He doesn't pull it, but keeps it just so taut that he can feel the movements of Number 2 as he climbs. So Number 2 is safe—even if he slips and dangles, Number 1 will be able to hold fast until he regains his holds, or if necessary lower him down to the stance below.

Notice the attitude of Number 2. He is standing up straight on his footholds, not leaning in or hugging the rock-face. This attitude is the key to good rock-climbing, for it means that the climber is *in balance*. The art is to be always dependent on the feet, even if the holds are small, rather than on the hands, which should be used mainly for maintaining the balance instead of for clutching and muscling up. Number 2, standing well away from the rock, is much less likely to slip than if he was leaning inwards, and he can also see where his next holds will be and so move upwards smoothly and continuously. Progressing by a series of violent jerks and gasping pauses is bad climbing. Of course, in chimneys and cracks and awkward places of that sort it may very well be necessary to adopt strange attitudes and make tremendous efforts; but in "open climbing," whether on rock or snow or ice, *stand up straight* is the Golden Rule for safety.

The rope, secured to the waist of Number 2 with an overhand knot or (much better) an Alpine Butterfly knot, drops its slack to Number 3, sometimes called "the anchor man." Number 3, it will be seen, has his nose in the air; he is carefully watching all the movements of Number 2 so that when his turn comes to climb he will have a good idea of where the difficult moves come and how to deal with them. He is belayed, like Number 1, to a rock spike on the stance, but not so securely, because the belay spike is below his waist-level. It is better to have a belay above the climber, because then he cannot be pulled off his stance at all. Number 3 is paying out the rope as Number 2 climbs, and he must see that it runs freely and doesn't jerk the man above.

When Number 2 reaches the stance where the Leader is, he makes an overhand loop and slips it under the Leader's loop on the spike. If there is room for all three on the platform, Number 3 may climb up to join them, belayed as he comes by Number 2; but more usually the Leader will take off his belay loop—Number 2 at once taking the rope and safeguarding him—and start to climb the next pitch. Number 2 (known as the Second) pays out the rope round his shoulder as the Leader climbs, and gives all his attention to him until he reaches the next stance and calls down to say he is securely belayed there. Then the Second brings up Number 3. And so on, one man moving at a time up the pitches of the route.

Now it can be seen why the Leader must be the best climber. He alone is in any danger if he slips. And yet, if he falls, his Second has a good chance of holding him. The fierce jerk of the fall would come on the Second's hands and body, probably pulling him off his balance. But the belay from his waist to the solid rock will save him from being pulled down. In such an accident all may depend on the rope. It *must* be a good one.

In practice, a Leader very seldom falls. He is prudent enough, if he is a good mountaineer, to undertake only such ascents as are within his powers. One of the things you must learn as you go along is the standard of climb you are able to tackle. There is a lot more to learn, too, as you'll find out. But if you read and remember the things set down in the foregoing five paragraphs, and act on them, you'll make a good showing on your first rock climb—and you'll know the basic method of all mountain climbing, whether it's on a Welsh crag or on Everest.

118

Snow and Ice

There are many rock climbers who are not really mountaineers. The problem of a rock-face is all that interests them, and the thrills of the summit or of winter and Alpine climbing are not for them. They miss an enormous amount of fun. A Senior Scout, Looking Wide, will want to make himself an average all-round mountaineer rather than a super-expert rock-climber. And on British mountains in winter he has the chance of learning how.

Again, someone who knows the ropes should be found to lead. And an additional item of equipment will be needed—an Ice Axe. Good ex-Army axes can be obtained for about £1. When you know how to use your axe you are made free of the mountains when winter grips them, as well as in summer. The principle of climbing a steep slope of snow (the "ice" sometimes met with is really only very hard-frozen snow) is the same as for rock-climbing, but the details are different. On snow you make your own footholds by cutting steps, and your own belays by thrusting in the ice axe so that a rope loop placed over it gives a sound protection.

One good way of getting into real Alpine climbing quickly is to take a holiday in Austria with a party, with an experienced leader or guide. The mountains there are fine—over 10,000 feet but not unduly difficult. You could write to Ingham Ltd., of 143 New Bond Street, London, W.1, who are representatives of the Austrian Alpine Club, to find out what courses are being run in the summer. Usually there are three grades: one for walkers only, one for those who want to begin Alpine climbing, and one for fairly experienced climbers.

Mountaineers Look Wide

And then you are on the threshold of a new world of adventure. All the hundreds of fine mountains await your conquest, and a thousand hours of the most magnificent sport will be yours. It doesn't matter that all the European peaks have been climbed many times before. Each season they are new and different—indeed, no mountain is ever quite the same on one day as it was the day before. Weather, snow conditions, rock changes, all conspire to make your ascent different from anyone else's. And European mountains aren't the only ones.

No sport has such a wide field of new adventure in front of it as mountaineering. There are literally hundreds of virgin peaks over 20,000 feet high in the Himalayas, and unnumbered lesser mountains. Why shouldn't you aim, now, at getting to the Himalayas sometime? If you are keen enough, it can be done, even if you aren't asked to join an expedition. Think of running your own! It's likely to cost £400 per man, but what of that? Suppose, just suppose, you could manage to save £50 a year when you start earning. In eight years—when you're twenty-five, say—you'd have enough, and the experience of a lifetime would be within your grasp. I'm not talking through my hat, because I did it, in 1954. I left it rather late to start saving, though, and was forty-six years old when my chance came.

"Don't keep your nose glued to the piece of rock in front of you."

So if you really intend to make Mountaineering your sport, don't keep your nose glued to the bit of rock in front of you. Look at the view. Look to the horizon and the peaks beyond it. Plan ahead—and start now!

BOOKS TO READ

ON MOUNTAINCRAFT:

Introduction to Mountaineering, by Showell Styles (Seeley Service).
Climbing in Britain, by J. E. Q. Barford (Penguin).
The Mountaineer's Week-End Book, by Showell Styles (Seeley Service).
Mountain Craft, by G. Winthrop Young (Methuen).

On Mountain Adventure:

The Conquest of Everest, by Sir John Hunt.

My Climbs in the Alps and Caucasus, by A. F. Mummery.

The Ascent of Nanda Devi, by H. W. Tilman.

On High Hills, by G. Winthrop Young.

British Crags and Climbers, edited by E. C. Pyatt and Wilfred Noyce.

Chapter 13

CAVING

CAVING is unique among the outdoor pastimes such as walking and climbing, for there is always the possibility of real exploration of the unknown. Even the remotest mountains of Britain have probably sometime been visited by man; but underground it is always possible that no one has noticed a small branch-passage or a climb up in the roof. Often one's hopes are dashed by discovering a footprint or a torch-battery at the far end; but a rush of flood-water or a fall of rock can reveal unvisited passages, and excavation may do the same.

Books written for boys of twelve frequently use caves to provide a thrilling background for the story. Even as we grow older the attraction of the unknown remains; but to some perhaps the idea of exploring caves seems rather childish. There is, however, a vast difference between a casual exploration of a short cave with a torch or just a box of matches, and a planned "caving" trip. Enthusiasts treat caving just as seriously as others treat cycling or mountaineering. Adventure may be the main attraction, but the discipline and techniques are absorbing and also valuable training.

"Mountaineering in reverse."

Pot-holing is the name given to the sport in Yorkshire, because there many of the caves are entered down a vertical "pot" — a water-eroded shaft. "Mountaineering in reverse" is a good description, for it also emphasises that the thought and equipment which a mountaineer considers necessary for a major mountain ascent are also needed for an underground trip which may take all day—or all night—and entail vertical pitches (shafts) and awkward traverses (crossings of ledges). The pitches are usually water-polished and unclimbable, requiring rope-ladders and ropes.

Most caving clubs refuse to accept boys under sixteen as members, and this should be a guide to leaders who are considering taking boys underground. Considerable stamina and physical strength are needed for any but minor caving visits. This is not to say that cavers need be super-men; but the endurance of the weakest member of the party must be considered as the factor which limits what the party should try to undertake. A boy of twelve may cope with many of the difficulties of a cave, but he lacks the length of arm and leg of an older boy, and he cannot carry his share of the tackle. He does not realise the danger to others which careless acts may cause, and he cannot be relied upon in tying tackle or holding another member of the party on a life-line. Age will remedy the physical handicaps, and the process of learning to become a responsible member of a caving team is a very valuable experience.

LEADERS

A leader with knowledge and practical experience is essential if a great deal of waste of time and possible danger are to be avoided. Small-scale visits to minor caves may satisfy some and give useful training, but sooner or later the keener cavers will want to tackle something bigger. A leader without experience carries a heavy load of responsibility. For him the best place to gain experience is in a reputable caving club and there profit from the accumulated knowledge of its experienced members. He will then be able to lead and train others with confidence.

The Cave Research Group was founded largely to provide a clearing-house for information regarding caves. Its Secretary, Dr. G. T. Warwick, of the Department of Geography, University of Birmingham, can give the

123

addresses of club secretaries in all caving areas.[1] Most clubs will gladly give advice to parties of cavers who may wish to visit their areas. They may have surveys of the caves and may even offer to lend some tackle; but what they do not welcome is to be asked to take a whole crowd of unknown learners down a difficult pot-hole. This is more than anyone should expect.

These pieces of advice will probably be quite unnecessary to Scouts who live near the caving and pot-holing grounds, but apply particularly to those who live farther away and may contemplate a camp near caves.

Do not be too proud to make use of whatever surveys or sketch-plans may be available. If you borrow one, make

"A cold, damp job."

a copy to take underground, and add to it when you can. If none is available, make your own on the spot, and let the club which could not (or would not) supply you have a copy of yours. Cave surveying is quite fascinating, but tends to be a cold, damp job. An accurate survey may be very useful to scientists, but a rough plan is also well worth having. Detailed methods are described in *British Caving*,[2] but for most purposes a simple traverse, using a prismatic compass and measuring tape, is satisfactory. Whatever methods were used should be stated on your plan (and elevations and sections, if any), so that other people will know how accurate it is likely to be. The C.R.G. also welcomes reports.[1]

LOCATION

Most of the caves and pot-holes are found in the Carboniferous Limestone outcrops. The Craven district of Yorkshire has nearly 400 cave-systems, many of them containing active streams and vertical pitches. Many of the caves in the Peak District of Derbyshire are around

124

Castleton and Matlock. Four other major caving areas
are: South Wales, outside the coal-mining area; the
Mendips; County Clare; and the Sligo-Fermanagh area.
Caves also occur in other parts of Ireland, in the North-
West Highlands of Scotland, North Wales and South
Devon. A detailed list of caves and the tackle needed for
each is provided by *Britain Underground*.[3]

In most city public libraries it is possible to view on
request the quarter-inch geological maps of the area, and
on these you will see the outcrop of Carboniferous Limestones. The limestones, however, represented by pale blue,
are not equally permeable by water. In Craven, the upper
strata, the Yoredale series, are 950 feet thick and do not
produce significant caves. The Great Scar Limestone
beneath, however, has caves at many levels throughout
its 600 feet. When streams run off the impervious rocks
they usually disappear down pot-holes in the limestone
and sometimes can be traced emerging at its base. Most
of them are north of the line Settle-Grassington and south
of Sedbergh-Kettlewell.

The following are some suggestions to start with. There
are "show" caves near Pateley Bridge, Ingleton and
Clapham, for which, of course, one has to pay but needs
no tackle. Easy caves where only the farmers' approval
need be sought are Douk Cave, near Kettlewell in
Wharfedale, and the Long Churn Cave as far as the
45-foot Dolly Tubs pitch into Alum Pot (which should not
be attempted without ropes and ladders). A really worthwhile but simple pot is Calf Holes (Dry Laithe Hole),
near Old Ing Farm about four miles north of Horton-in-
Ribblesdale. This requires tackle for a 35-foot pitch.

The Derbyshire "Dome" of limestone has few pot-holes
but a number of comparatively small but interesting caves.
In Castleton there are three show-caves, all worth a visit.
Giant's Hole, near Peakshill Farm, is a sporting cave,
and so is the partly-commercialised Bagshawe Cavern in
Bradwell.

In Mendip the limestone is very strongly folded.
Wookey Hole and the Cheddar Gorge show-caves are

125

well known. There are many other small caves nearby, but the longer ones need care. Wherever a low section would be flooded and become impassable after heavy rain, the suitability of the weather must be considered. In South Wales the limestone forms a great elongated basin with an outcrop only about a mile wide in the north. The sea caves of Gower are well known, but more exciting are the more extensive caverns up the valleys. Dan-y-Ogof in the upper Tawe valley needs wading, swimming or a rubber dinghy for the third lake. Will's Hole in the Neath valley near Pont Neath Vaughan needs tackle for a 35-foot pitch.

In Devon there are several clusters of caves in the Devonian Limestone. Near Buckfastleigh there is a considerable choice of easy caves and more complex ones like Baker's Pit and Reed's. Permission should be sought in all cases. Kent's Cavern, near Torquay, is a fine show-cave.

Most of the known Scottish caves are in the Cambrian Limestone along the line of the Moine Thrust, as at Durness and near Inchnadamph in Sutherland.

The caves and pot-holes of Ireland are described in detail in *British Caving,* to which reference should be made also for further information about all the regions; but two areas may be suggested here as worthy of visits: the Marble Arch area in Fermanagh in Northern Ireland, and the region around Slieve Elva in County Clare, which includes Ireland's longest cave, Pollnagollum.

PERSONAL EQUIPMENT

"Take a complete change of clothes."

A caver should always take a complete change of clothes with him and not expect to wear any of his ordinary clothes underground. Mud and water usually make one's caving clothing unwearable for any other purpose afterwards. The minimum personal equipment should include warm,

126

tough garments, strong nailed boots, a hat capable of absorbing hard knocks, and a reliable lamp. Bathing trunks and woollen underclothes (even long pants), a strong shirt and trousers (rather than shorts) are recommended. A semi-waterproof jacket is useful; and a boiler suit holds everything together, excludes some of the mud, has buttoning pockets and prevents clothes rucking up if one has to come out feet first from a crawl. Warmth is emphasised because ladder pitches in particular cause waits which often seem to be in a cold draught.

Clinker nails are as good as any on climbing-boots, but moulded rubber composition soles have also proved suitable. The best headgear is a miner's fibre helmet with a lamp mounted on it.[4] Electric and acetylene lamps can be bought, but are rather expensive and it is not difficult to improvise a lamp to fit on the helmet and connect to a 3-cell dry battery in a pocket. Spare bulbs, matches in a waterproof tin, and a candle or two should be carried. Useful also are a short length of life-line looped round the waist with a karabiner (steel ring with hinged spring-loaded portion), and a whistle.

Always take a ration of food with you, such as chocolate, dried bananas, raisins and dates. For a trip of more than three hours it is best to pack sandwiches in a tin and carry this in a small haversack. Equip yourself to prepare hot drinks and a good meal when you come out.

GENERAL EQUIPMENT AND ITS USE

Steep slopes and short climbable but slippery rock steps should have a securely belayed rope to act as a hand-line. Vertical pitches must be climbed by a ladder, and on a pitch longer than about twenty feet each caver should normally use a life-line. Any fit and active person can safely climb fifty feet in fair conditions, but a falling stone can put one hand temporarily out of action for instance, and if one man does not use the life-line, another who is tired may not like to ask for the life-line either. The ladder and the top end of the life-line and the man paying it out

127

or pulling it up must each be independently belayed to a sound rock mass or wedged timber.

Avoid complicated knots; readjustments frequently have to be made. Where available, nothing is more convenient than a wedged tree-trunk or pole from which to rig the rope-ladder. Clove-hitches should be reversed in sense to avoid the risk of rotating the timber.

Manilla ropes of $\frac{1}{2}$-inch to $\frac{5}{8}$-inch diameter are most commonly used in caves for all purposes: as life-lines, in wood-and-rope ladders, and for belaying. Nylon line is excellent for life-lines in experienced hands, but is expensive and should be carried in haversacks.

Making one's own ladders is more satisfactory than trying to buy them ready-made, for reasons of cost and because one values more what one has made. A simple ladder can be made by threading ropes through flat-drilled ash rungs and then binding the rope on both sides of the rung with twine to prevent slipping. Equally sound is to drive a pointed hickory peg through drilled holes in the rung and through the rope. Convenient measurements for the rope-ladder are a total of 25 feet plus rope-ends, and rungs spaced ten inches apart with nine inches between the ropes. All rope-ends should be whipped rather than spliced back to avoid catching in cracks and to facilitate tying.

For each pitch the life-line needs to be at least twenty feet longer than the pitch, so that useful lengths are 50, 75, 100 and 125 feet. Shorter lengths are useful for belaying ladders. All ropes should be carried carefully coiled and tied in two places. Ladders should be tightly coiled for carrying also, but, like the ropes, need to be loosened and hung on pegs (not nails) in an airy place to dry afterwards.

It is vitally important that the life-lining should be properly done. Needless to say, perhaps, the knot to use when tying a rope round one's middle is a bowline, and the rope should be tight round the waist. The man paying it out (or in) should keep the rope taut enough to be able to feel the climber's movements. He must sit or stand so that a sudden jerk cannot dislodge him, and for additional security he should use his sling or the top end of the life-line or a separate rope to belay himself to something firm and independent of the ladder. The rope from the man on the ladder should be held at waist-level by one hand; it should then pass across the life-liner's back and forward over the opposite shoulder to the other hand. It should not be allowed to slide through the hands, but should be gripped firmly and paid out carefully.

On a long pitch and near falling water, whistle signals must be used by the climber:

> One blast = stop.
>
> Two blasts = pull.
>
> Three blasts = pay out the rope.

When he has reached the bottom and untied the line, two blasts will also get the line pulled up.

On long pitches a rope should be attached to each side of the ladder at 100 f et from the top to take the weight of the lower part of the ladder and to assist in pulling the tackle up. Not more than one person at a time should be allowed on the ladder.

ORGANISATION & METHODS

Caving by yourself is not wise, particularly if you have not left word with anyone where you are going. If you leave a note at the entrance stating when you went in, this may save you if, for instance, you get trapped by a fall of rock or by flood water;

"Caving by yourself is not wise."

but do remember to destroy the note afterwards. Teams of five or six are good, and a personal knowledge of one another's strong and weak points acquired by working together makes the team infinitely stronger than it would be otherwise.

From start to finish there should be no doubt who is

E

the leader of the party, and his word must be law; but he may decide to lead from behind and let another experienced caver go first. It is in general wise to leave someone above ground and also at the head of each pitch, firstly to prevent passing hikers from throwing stones down the hole, secondly to avoid the last man down and the first man up having to climb without a life-line. An alternative is, of course, to use a pulley-block and a life-line more than double the length of the pitch. Towards the end of a long caving trip one can easily become careless; no one should hesitate to ask for a life-line if he wants one.

Haste and inefficient lights are the two factors most likely to lead to trouble; so plan your trip carefully and take spare batteries. If most of the lights in the party become unserviceable, the wisest plan is to find as dry a spot as possible for the majority of the party and for two to take serviceable lamps and get to the surface as quickly as possible and fetch replacements. To move without lights is courting disaster. Such lack of foresight should never occur, but it has occurred and no doubt will again.

FORMATION OF CAVES

Apart from sea caves which may occur in almost any kind of solid rock, almost all the penetrable caves are found in limestone. It is believed that the latter are formed by water, first penetrating along cracks in the limestone and then enlarging them by solution. As movement of water grows, the enlarged cracks develop into tubes and cavities. Grit and pebbles are washed in and play their part in wearing a channel. Limestone tends to have a rectangular pattern of joints so that cave systems also seem to have a rectangular plan and section. Solution and erosion are known to take place deep down, even below the levels where the rock is permanently saturated. Many cave systems such as Gaping Gill begin as a vertical shaft engulfing a stream; they continue as passages which can be followed part of the way and end with a submerged section leading to a mouth in the valley below. Many others have insignificant beginnings which necessitate a tight squeeze through narrow passages; some start as impenetrable pebbly sinks or cracks in the bed of a stream and can be explored only from the lower end where the stream emerges. Very few indeed can be followed through from sink to resurgence.

Most people know that stalactites are the formations which grow like icicles from the roof of caves, and that stalagmites are the usually thicker upward-growing masses of calcite. They owe their growth to the fact that ground water contains dissolved carbon dioxide, and it dissolves limestone as it percolates downwards in proportion to the amount of carbon dioxide it contains. When the water emerges through the roof of a cave it often loses some of its carbon dioxide into the air and deposits a calcite film on the roof. This may take the form of a skin over a wall or a ring round a drip which grows into a hollow straw-like stalactite. If the latter becomes blocked, the stalactite may thicken and grow into what show-cave guides like to christen "The Elephant's Trunk" or the "Sword of Damocles." Falling drips also build up the stalagmite bosses on the floor. Eccentric or distorted stalactites are usually known as helictites. Occasionally upward and downward growths meet and form beautiful calcite columns. Calcite is the commonest crystalline form of calcium carbonate.

These are familiar forms of calcite, but they are not the only ones to be seen in caves. Films of calcite form over the walls, and the flow continues out across the floor and down the cave passage. Boulders become cemented as if by milk; rippled slopes of the "flowstone" bulge from the walls where the flow is greatest; and pools with a gentle flow grow crystalline rims. These formations in particular are very fragile, and unseeing boots can soon ruin some of Nature's most beautiful handiwork.

In the interest of others who will follow and will hope to enjoy what you have found, try to avoid muddying the dripstone formations and keep to one track across encrusted floors. Above all, do not break what has taken many years to grow.

Remember, too, that there are many lines of scientific research which can be followed underground; you probably will in time develop an interest in one or more, but in any case do not let thoughtlessness hinder others. For instance, many small forms of life are not found above ground, and used carbide is not likely to make their pool life more tasteful. It may exterminate something which was rare. Photographs form a permanent and beautiful record of a cave, and are just as satisfying as specimens.

RESCUE

Every member of a caving or pot-holing party should know whether there is a local rescue organisation and where its headquarters are.

In Yorkshire the Settle police should be informed if there is an accident (Telephone: Settle 2122). From there the Cave Rescue Organisation, the R.A.F. Mountain Rescue Unit from Topcliffe and the Upper Wharfedale Fell Rescue Association from Grassington will be called into action as required.

Wells police (Telephone: Wells 2197) will initiate rescue work in the Mendips, where the Wessex Cave Club, the University of Bristol Spelaeological Society, the Bristol Exploration Club and the Mendip Nature Research Committee jointly organise help.

The South Wales Cave Rescue Organisation has its headquarters at Pen-y-Cae at the head of the Swansea Valley. Given full information the police will set rescue work in motion.

At Buckfastleigh, the Devon Rescue Group has been formed by the Devon Spelaeological Society, and contact should be made via Ashburton police (Telephone: Ashburton 210).

In the event of an accident the first action should be to find out as far as possible exactly what is the matter, then send a message to the surface stating what has happened and what help is needed. As soon as first-aid measures have been applied, the movement of an injured person toward the surface should be begun, unless of course a stretcher is essential. Calmness, warmth and action, if this is possible, will encourage the patient. As soon as possible, dry clothes and hot-water bottles should be got to the injured person, and hot drinks and food for the rescuers also should not be forgotten. An efficient organiser of the rescue efforts must stay on the surface and ensure a steady flow of rescue teams and information.

REFERENCES

[1] The Secretary of Cave Research Group is Dr. G. T. Warwick, Department of Geography, University of Birmingham, 341 Bristol Road, Birmingham 5.

[2] *British Caving,* by Members of Cave Research Group (Routledge and Kegan Paul), 1953, 35s.

[3] *Britain Underground*, by Norman Thornber and others (Dalesman Publishing Co.), 1953, 7s. 6d.

[4] Cromwell Protector Helmets are obtainable from Helmets Ltd., Moat Factory, Wheathampstead, St. Albans, Herts.

MOUNTAINEER'S BADGE TEST REQUIREMENTS
(CAVING)

(1) Be familiar with one extensive system of caves, or two minor ones.

(2) Discuss kit, ropes and rope-ladders, knots, windlass, derrick, lights and suitable food.

(3) Demonstrate emergency actions and how to walk in darkness; removal of injured persons. Discuss the dangers which exist.

(4) Know how pot-holes are formed, including caves, swallets, trefoils, etc., and describe two of the better-known systems.

(5) Discuss geological and mineralogical aspects, fossilisation and formation of stalactites and stalagmites.

(6) Take part in five explorations and produce log-book.

Chapter 14

THE WORLD OF NATURE

IT is difficult to write a brief but comprehensive account about the world of nature. The variety of living things is so vast, so complex, that new species and forms are being constantly discovered. If you were to spend a whole lifetime studying the important works that have been written on natural history—and if you could remember all they contain—you would then be only on the fringe of knowledge; for as soon as you have learnt a little about one aspect of the subject, countless other aspects begin to present themselves. That is the challenge confronting every naturalist, whether he is a novice or an acknowledged authority. There is no end to your search, no final solution to many of the problems that arise, even if you confine yourself to the habits of a single species.

But the vast scope of nature is one of its attractions. Once you have taken it up, either as a spare-time hobby or a lifetime's work, it will absorb you completely. Each discovery will whet your appetite and increase your enthusiasm; each failure to unravel a problem will spur you on to greater effort. In this endless and exciting field of enquiry you will find a thousand adventures and surprises. You will gain a deeper insight into the marvels and mysteries of creation and learn something about the ever-changing face of the countryside. Most important of all, you will enjoy a rich source of physical and mental refreshment.

All this may seem obvious enough to those who have made the experiment. I also realise that it has always been an essential part of Scout philosophy and training to encourage an interest in wild life and a genuine appreciation of the countryside. But what of our nation as a whole? How have we treated this priceless heritage? The answer is important because it reveals a state of affairs from which we can learn some useful lessons.

"Take an interest in wild life."

A foreign visitor to England once remarked to me that the British people were an extraordinary mixture of contradictions. We had a wonderful diversity of scenery for so small a country—but how little we took care of it! Probably we were kinder to domestic animals than the average German, Italian or Frenchman, even to the point of being sentimental—but how indifferent we were about the preservation of wild creatures and plants! Admittedly, there were some notable exceptions to this general attitude. Most species of birds were protected by Act of Parliament, and the grey seal (alone of British mammals) was also protected by law during its breeding season. But as for butterflies, flowers and the rest: anyone could collect or destroy them at will except on National Trust property and on a few special nature reserves.

My friend went on to say that our huge, sprawling cities and congested streets were a regrettable and perhaps unavoidable evil, but what really shocked him was the way in which we had allowed so many of our suburbs to stretch their tentacles outwards until the arterial roads joining towns and outlying villages had become defaced by a continuous rash of red-roofed villas and jerry-built houses in the worst possible taste. Surely this showed a complete disregard for natural beauty!

I explained that much of the ribbon development from which we now suffer had occurred after the First World War when the speculative builder had been able to do pretty well as he liked. Certainly it was all rather shameful, but things were now much improved. Today we had our Town and Country Planning Acts, our scheduled Green Belts and National Parks. I also pointed out that during the last twenty years the British nation had

135

become more concerned about wild life and that dozens of thriving natural history societies now existed to study and preserve it—to say nothing about the growing numbers of enthusiasts who went out on their own at weekends to observe wild creatures and plants.

I do not know whether I succeeded in convincing my friend that things are better than they used to be. Being a visitor in a foreign land, perhaps he was too polite to disagree with me, but, judging by the expression on his face, I guessed he thought the British public were still inclined to be somewhat insensitive—or, at any rate, forgetful—about the world of nature.

Unfortunately, it is true that until recent times we have hardly troubled to preserve our countryside and its wild inhabitants, but have taken them for granted. When the Industrial Revolution of the nineteenth century changed us from an agricultural nation into a community mainly of city-dwellers, there was no national outcry against the wholesale destruction of natural beauty. We were too busy laying the foundations of our commercial and industrial wealth to consider such matters. Before long we had transformed vast areas of fertile land into an unsightly mass of factory buildings and slag-heaps devoid of wild life except for the few species that could manage to adapt themselves to such conditions.

Although the rapid expansion of cities and towns has produced an unsightly blot in many places, we must remember that even our dwindling acres of countryside, which may look unspoilt in comparison, are largely an artificial creation. Arable land, grazing pastures and many of our forests bear the stamp of man's influence on the natural scene—an influence which began long before the Industrial Revolution. In some cases the physical effects of these man-made changes are pleasing enough to the eye. The old country estates with their fine mansions, timbered parks and ornamental lakes have an imposing beauty; the fields of rich grass and growing crops surrounded by neatly-trimmed hedges make a charming pastoral scene; and the great reservoirs which supply water and electric power to the urban districts often look attractive when set among mountains and hills. Indeed, when you come to think about it, there is not much countryside left that can be called wild in the literal sense of the word.

To find really virgin land you must visit the moorlands of the North and West Country, the uncultivated parts of the Scottish and Welsh highlands, the undrained fens of East Anglia and the more remote stretches of coastline. In such areas wild life undergoes changes with the passing of time because nature never remains static, but many of these variations have little or nothing to do with the agency of man. Some animal populations have natural cycles of prosperity and depression. In certain years a species becomes plentiful; in others its numbers are drastically reduced. Disease and other factors contribute their share to these cycles which seem to be fairly regular among small mammals, such as field-voles and other rodents. Then there is the weather. Have you ever noticed that during prolonged spells of severe frost redwings and fieldfares (two of our common winter migrants) sometimes die in large numbers? Or that after a late frost in April there are fewer young birds to be seen? Nature herself often plays a hand in the game of control so that only the hardy and forceful specimens shall survive to carry on the race.

In cultivated districts changes in animal populations are sometimes swifter and more dramatic than in really wild territory because artificial factors are superimposed on the natural pattern of variation. Take the Forestry Commission plantations, for example. What was once a bare strip of land soon becomes covered with luxuriant (if somewhat regimented) foliage. These forests are attractive to woodland creatures but discourage species that prefer more open country. Thus a sudden change occurs in the local animal and plant life. Similarly with reservoirs. Water-loving species increase where land creatures formerly dwelt and the pattern of living things undergoes a radical upheaval. I could give several other examples if space allowed, and you can probably think of some yourself.

137

I have dealt at some length with the changing face of Britain because it may help you to understand more clearly the setting in which our native creatures live and against which they often have to contend. The study of their habits in relation to their environment is called ecology—but do not be put off by the name. It is a fascinating subject because it shows us how living things react to various causes, whether natural or artificial. To understand properly the habits of a small group of creatures or the habits of only one species belonging to that group we need to know about its reactions to other groups and the effects produced on them all by changes in habitat and food supply. These problems offer the student of wild life a wonderful opportunity to make a really outstanding contribution to scientific knowledge.

But the chap who is just starting to take an interest in natural history will probably want to approach it from a rather different angle. The interplay between one form of life and another may seem too ambitious a subject for him to tackle at the beginning. He will be more concerned with identifying and recording the species he sees. He will also want to know how to go about it and what to look for in his own district. Then, after he has done some of this groundwork, he may turn his attention more fully to the study of ecology and other problems.

There are certain golden rules which everyone who wants to be a good naturalist must learn until they become

"Observe without being observed."

an instinctive part of him. The most important of these is to observe without being observed. Never hurry unless you must. The man who dashes about sees little, but he will certainly be seen or heard by the creatures he wants to watch.

Most birds and mammals are very shy. Experience has taught them to be quick-witted

and elusive if they are to survive the con-
stant dangers that beset them. Whether
you like it or not, they regard you as an
enemy, or at least as a potential threat to
their security, so you must practise the art
of blending with your surroundings.

"Most birds or mammals are very shy."

The average person who goes for a walk
in the country hardly ever bothers to make
himself inconspicuous, and even some
naturalists seem to underestimate the importance of camouflage. Wild creatures
are quick to detect an object moving on the skyline; never
poke your head up suddenly in such a situation or make
an erratic gesture with the hand. If taken unawares in an
open space where there is little or no cover, you should
crouch on the ground and make yourself as small as
possible. I once read of a bird-watcher who lay so motionless in an open field that a raven pitched a few yards from
him, quite unperturbed; but such a feat is surely rare!

The mention of camouflage naturally brings me to the
subject of clothes. Brown tweeds and grey flannels are
both suitable, but materials of almost any dull shade will
do. Of course you are likely to defeat your object if you
put on dark trousers but wear a white or brightly-coloured
shirt without a jacket! During hot weather most of us
like to take our jackets off, but if you do so be sure that
your shirt is dark or khaki-coloured. Mammals and birds
are suspicious of bright objects, especially moving ones,
and when I was a beginner I remember scaring off a
woodpecker at close range because I was foolish enough
to use my pocket-handkerchief at the wrong moment!

Although birds do not seem to have much sense of
smell, it is a very different matter when you are watching
mammals. They can pick up your scent at a considerable
distance and therefore you must be careful to choose a
vantage-point where the wind blows *towards* you, otherwise you may be wasting your time. In spite of their keen
sense of smell, some mammals are inclined to be short-
sighted, and I have often been surprised to find how close

one can get to badgers and otters before they become aware of it. But you must certainly not regard this as a general rule. Deer, for example, are very keen-sighted, and so are birds.

Perhaps it is hardly necessary to stress the need for silence when you are studying wild creatures. All the same, you may find it difficult to walk quietly on ground where there are dead twigs or branches that snap with a sound like miniature rifle-fire when stepped on. With practice you can become quite expert at treading softly, and personally I often wear a pair of rubber-soled shoes when visiting woods or stony ground. Not only do they make less noise, but they also help to keep out the damp.

Now for a few words about the sense faculties you will need to develop if you want to become a successful observer. Obviously you must train your eyes and ears. Many creatures have a habit of vanishing suddenly after showing themselves for a few seconds. Unless you are alert you may miss seeing them altogether, or, worse still, you may get a brief glimpse of something interesting but fail to notice it properly. I have sometimes heard naturalists say: "I think it was a so-and-so, but I saw it too late to make sure." Such experiences are annoying and can often be avoided if you keep a sharp look-out and listen carefully. Good hearing is as important as keen sight, because many birds and mammals give themselves away by their voices.

"Cultivate the virtue of patience."

Every naturalist must cultivate the virtue of patience. Of course, you cannot expect to be lucky every time you go out to watch wild life, but it is surprising how much you will see if you are prepared to sit down and wait. Perhaps a faint needle-sharp squeak will betray the presence of a field-mouse running nimbly along a bank or climbing among the twigs of some bush. The squeak may be a signal to other mice or it may indicate that a weasel or stoat is on the prowl nearby. Watch carefully and with a bit of luck you may see the attacker running forward with leaps and bounds as it follows the scent of its quarry. Such sights are not uncommon provided you sit absolutely still for a considerable time. The art of remaining motionless for long periods is not easily acquired, but once you have mastered it you will find that even the shyest animals will venture close to you.

Two pieces of equipment are essential for watching birds and mammals: a notebook and a pair of field-glasses. The latter are likely to cost you quite a lot of money unless you can persuade your parents to give them to you. If you look after them properly they should last for years. Prismatic binoculars are much better than the old-fashioned types, because they give a wider field of vision, which means more light-gathering power. If you examine a pair of prismatic field-glasses you will notice that they are usually engraved with the magnification power, followed by the diameter—e.g. 6 x 30, 8 x 50, and so on. If you divide the larger number by the smaller one you will get what is called the "key" figure. A key figure between 4 and 7 is adequate, and you do not need a pair of field-glasses with a very high magnification. Apart from being very expensive they are also heavy and tiring to hold.

Always buy field-glasses of a reputable brand because then you can be sure that they are reliable. You may be able to get a good second-hand pair from a dealer in optical instruments at a greatly reduced price, but if you decide to save money in this way, be sure to take someone with you to the shop who knows what points to look for and can advise you on your choice. There are some good bargains to be found, but field-glasses (like most other second-hand articles) must be selected with care. I would also advise you to read the excellent little booklet by E. M. Nicholson, called *How to Choose and Use Field-Glasses."* It costs only ninepence and is published by the British Trust for Ornithology, 2 King Edward St., Oxford.

141

It is a good plan to protect your notebook with a waterproof covering in case you get wet, which is always likely to happen in our British climate! If you see a bird that you cannot recognise, you should make a rough sketch of it on the spot, adding notes about its size, colour and markings, together with other relevant facts: place where seen, flight, voice, and so forth. It is much better to do this while the memory of the specimen is fresh in your mind, rather than trust to your recollection later. The same general drill can be adapted to cover any form of wild life you come across.

In order to identify unfamiliar species you will certainly need to consult a good book dealing with the appropriate group. New reference books on natural history with illustrations are rather expensive nowadays, but do not be discouraged. Your local public library will probably stock quite a good selection, and in any case the librarian will be able to obtain almost any modern standard work you want. Explain your requirements carefully and he will gladly advise you. Of course, if you can build up a small library of your own, so much the better.

I said at the beginning that the world of nature is too big a subject to deal with adequately in a few pages, but I hope I have written enough to awaken your interest. Good hunting!

Part 3

THE CRITICAL ATTITUDE

Chapter 15

READING

"Books are the best friends a man can have. You choose those that you like; you can rely on them at all times; they can help you in your work, in your leisure, and in your sorrow. You have them always around you at your beck and call in your home. They are not nowadays very expensive if you only buy one now and then to make up your collection. At any rate, the nearest public library will bring almost any book to your hand without expense." (B.-P.'s OUTLOOK, *October,* 1932.)

". . . and lo! a bright fire burning, and, smiling over against the blaze of it, cheerful, companionate, my books have been awaiting me."

(From "A CORNISH WINDOW" by Q.)

I

ONE wintry afternoon when I was about ten, I pulled down from a shelf at home a bound volume of the *Strand Magazine* and opened it by chance at a story called "The Red-Headed League," which I read lying on my stomach on the rug in front of a gay and friendly fire. Outside, the wet mist of a drab December afternoon was becoming mixed up with darkness; soon it would be time for tea and buttered toast. But I had found 221B Baker Street and had introduced myself to Dr. Watson and Mr. Sherlock Holmes: "Sherlock Holmes' quick eye took in my occupation and he shook his head as he noticed my questioning glances. 'Beyond the obvious fact that he has at some time done manual labour, that he takes snuff, that he is a Freemason, that he has been in China, and that he has done a considerable amount of writing lately, I can deduce nothing else'."

One of the presents I unwrapped on a Christmas morning long ago was a sombre, dull-black book with a paper label: *1914 and Other Poems by Rupert Brooke*; poetry, h'm . . . Until then, poetry hadn't interested me much: I had (like you, I expect) read some at school, had memorised some in the same way as I had memorised other things. At first all I admired about my new gift was the feel of the binding and the lovely thick rough paper. But then something extraordinary happened: I began reading the poetry inside and found myself not only liking it, but excited about it; I wanted to tell my friends about it. I had discovered a new world.

"I had discovered a new world."

(And perhaps I should add here, if you don't care for poetry yet, it's probably because you haven't discovered *your* sort of poetry, for poetry is as varied as the countryside: some fellows like bare downland swelling up to the sky, some the difficult paths of the high hills, some the calm waters of a wide estuary, others the coloured squares of a farm country or red cliffs and an angry sea. So it is with poetry: read all you can and one day you will find a poet who says things in such a way that you say, "Yes, that's exactly what I should have said if I could have said it"; he seems to see with your eyes, only more vividly and accurately. This is the important thing: that you can't know which poets you like until you start reading them to find out.)

Detective stories, poetry; two kinds of reading, but of course there are many more.

II

Let's consider prose, in which of course most of the books on the library shelves are written, and to fiction, which is what most people mean when they talk of books.

146

But *you* won't make that mistake! A writer of the present century has said: "There are men who analyse the nature of matter and men who classify demons. There are men who build bridges and men—women mostly—who ride on broomsticks. There are men who call the stars by name and men who measure their orbits. There are men who give the earth nitrates. There are men who give it blood. There are men who see trees as men walking, and there are men who see trees. There are men who can stop sickness, there are men who are immune from it. There are men who make art new, there is no man who can make a new art. There are men who can make an oar perfectly, there are men who can make us do without oars. There are men who can make horses obsolete. There are men who can ride. There are men who call a cold a punishment, a moral gymnasium or a nuisance. There are men who bless God and men God blessed." And she might have added: "Most of them have written books about themselves and their subjects."

I suppose from the dimmest days men have always wanted to listen to stories, and one's reading usually begins with stories short or long. The important thing is that one's reading shouldn't stop there, but should set out on voyages of discovery seeking out the real from the imagined, discovering how other men and women who were once as alive as you or I, not merely dream men and women who have and had no life outside the covers of the book they dwell in. But we all begin with stories or novels and here, too, spread your net wide and you will catch some strange and lovely fish: don't be satisfied with the same little shrimps you catch in that pool in the rocks you know so well. There are writers from France and Russia and America and China and Greece—to mention only a few—that you should know, and some of their books were written long, long ago.

"Plan your reading to keep the balance sane and sound."

147

But (and it is so important it must be said again) the reading of fiction is not the whole of reading, nor even a half of it. Plan your reading enough to keep the balance sane and sound. Letters, essays, history, diaries, plays, as well as short stories and long. It is sometimes said that books are not a substitute for life, but in fact they often have to be a substitute for a great part of life. From the days when I was knee-high to a duck I wanted to play cricket for my county, if not for England —as perhaps some of you do: but it was fairly obvious that my abilities were far distant from my dreams! But I can nevertheless enjoy half a loaf and read again and again about the great matches and the great players.

And I love mountains and wanted to climb them, but I shall never get farther than reading about those valiant attempts on the great peaks. So it will be with most of us.

III

To grow up without achieving the need to read a little at least every day is to deprive yourself of a great contentment and many true friends. The boy or man who loves books is never lonely, and never at a loss in a leisure hour. And he is constantly adding to his knowledge, dispersing the mists of ignorance that cling to our minds, widening his horizons, opening new windows on undreamed-of landscapes.

"A member of your local library."

You are naturally as an intelligent Senior Scout a member of your local Free or County Library, perhaps of a school library as well, so you'll be able to borrow them; if they're not on the shelves, the librarian will always help you to get them. But you'll find that you'll want to begin to *buy* books, to have (in fact) your own friends

148

at home on your own bookshelf. Getting together one's own small (but gradually increasing) library is an exciting and satisfying experience. Some, of course, will be reference books, a dictionary, an atlas, a book of quotations perhaps, but most of them will be books you want to have with you: companions you have chosen for life.

IV

Here, then, are fifty books I would recommend to you as Senior Scouts, with a motto "Look Wide" and a thirst for knowledge and adventure:—

1. *Three Men in a Boat,* by Jerome K. Jerome.
2. *The Longest Day (The Story of D-Day)* by Cornelius Ryan.
3. *South Col,* by Wilfred Noyce.
4. *The Riddle of the Sands,* by Erskine Childers.
5. *The Adventures (etc.) of Sherlock Holmes,* by Conan Doyle.
6. *The Thirty-Nine Steps,* by John Buchan.
7. *Operation Pax,* by Michael Innes.
8. *Ghost Stories of an Antiquary,* by M. R. James.
9. *Rogue Male,* by Geoffrey Household.
10. *Spanish Gold,* by George Birmingham.
11. *The Kon Tiki Expedition,* by Thor Heyerdahl.
12. *Above Us the Waves,* by Warren E. Benson.
13. *Collected Poems,* by John Masefield.
14. *Dam Busters,* by Paul Brickhill.
15. *Cache Lake Country,* by John J. Rowlands.
16. *The Silent World,* by M. Cousteau.
17. *Ten Years Under the Earth,* by N. Casteret.
18. *They Have Their Exits,* by Airey Neave.
19. *The Screwtape Letters,* by C. S. Lewis.
20. *Of Their Own Choice,* by Peter Churchill.
21. *Skis against the Atom,* by Knut Hankelid.
22. *Kim,* by Rudyard Kipling.
23. *The Father Brown Stories,* by G. K. Chesterton.
24. *The Experiences of an Irish R.M.,* by Somerville and Ross.
25. *The Day's Play,* by A. A. Milne.

149

26. *Jorkens in Africa*, by Lord Dunsany.
27. *Trent's Last Case*, by E. C. Bentley.
28. *The Gentle Art of Tramping*, by Stephen Grahame.
29. *English Saga*, by Arthur Bryant.
30. *The Worst Journey in the World*, by Cherry Apsley-Garrard.
31. *In the Land of Youth*, by James Stephens.
32. *The Open Road (an Anthology)*, by E. V. Lucas.
33. *Twenty Years a-Growin'*, by Maurice O'Sullivan.
34. *The Face is Familiar*, by Ogden Nash.
35. *Seven Years in Tibet*, by Heinrich Harrer.
36. *Collected Poems*, by John Betjeman.
37. *Who Moved the Stone?* by Frank Morison.
38. *Gods, Graves and Scholars*, by C. W. Ceram.
39. *The Little World of Don Camillo*, by Giovanni Guareschi.
40. *The Man Born to be King*, by Dorothy Sayers.
41. *Cream of Thurber*, by James Thurber.
42. *The Reason Why*, by C. Woodham-Smith.
43. *The Jungle is Neutral*, by F. Spencer Chapman.
44. *The Ballad of the White Horse*, by G. K. Chesterton.
45. *St. Joan*, by George Bernard Shaw.
46. *The Shetland Bus*, by David Howarth.
47. *Reach for the Sky*, by Paul Brickhill.
48. *Inspector Hanaud's Investigations*, by A. E. W. Mason.
49. *Beasts and Super Beasts*, by Saki.
50. *The Faber Book of Modern Verse*.

But remember, out of hundreds upon hundreds of thousands of books, this is a selection almost at random. There are many plays, volumes of poems, books about places and sport, about strange ways in other days and far-off shores which I could list for you equally quickly. The real answer is, of course, to go and search for yourself and find your own treasures and your own happiness among books—man's most dependable friends.

"Hundreds upon hundreds of thousands of books."

Chapter 16

THE ARTS

WE are often told that man is an animal; the highest of the mammals. This is a fact of which some people do not like to be too frequently reminded; they like to believe that there is a wide difference between man and the rest of the animal kingdom, and they express this difference by the use of such phrases as "homo sapiens" and "rational being." When we come to look at the matter closely, however, we find that we men have very much in common with the animals: we eat, drink, sleep, build homes, and we have to work to obtain the necessities of life; in fact, most of our waking hours are spent in the sheer business of keeping alive. So it is with nearly all animals. Even in our sport and recreation we resemble the brutes, for many animals and birds play, fight and dance just as we do. In all these things our ways are much more complicated than those of any of the animals; but the purpose and principle is the same. By far the greater part of our lives is spent in being animals, for there are hardly any of our activities which do not have counterparts in the animal world. Hardly any—but there are a few. "Rational being" is not quite an empty phrase, for there is a gulf between man and the brute. The difference consists partly in man's curiosity. That is not to say that animals are not curious—anyone who has camped in the same field as cows will testify to the curiosity of that creature! But only man has a burning desire to know the how and why of things; to understand his world. There are two other activities in which man stands alone. The first of these is the ability to love and worship God. The other is the ability to appreciate and to create beautiful things. I think it follows from this that the more of our

151

lives we devote to worshipping God, to acquiring knowledge and understanding, and to the pursuit of the arts, the farther we rise above the level of the animal; and that it is the degree of our success in these things which distinguishes us from the brute. If we go through our lives insensible and careless of the love of God, making no effort to grapple with the mysteries of life, and with our eyes and ears closed to the beauties of poetry, painting, sculpture and music, then no matter how successful we may become in a material sense; no matter how efficient at business or industry; no matter how much wealth, position and honour we acquire—we have nevertheless failed as human beings, and might almost as well have been a crisp cabbage or a clever codfish.

Having stressed the importance of the arts to our development as human beings, it may be of interest to devote a little space to differentiating between the true, or "fine" arts—literature, music, painting and sculpture—and their lesser counterparts. These counterparts consist of applied art, and popular or folk art. The basic difference is one of purpose. The purpose behind fine art is to uplift the spirit, to give expression to a great truth, or to provide a flash of divine illumination on some aspect of life; fine art is hardly ever useful in a material sense. Applied art, of course, is always useful; it includes architecture, and also the decorative arts such as ceramics, furniture, textiles, and so on. The purpose behind popular or folk art is to entertain, amuse, or give pleasure. This group is a very large one, including widely different things, such as most (although not quite all) films, light music, dance music, swing, jazz, posters, popular novels, comics, and so forth. Each of the fine arts has its popular counterpart, and these have existed for a very long time, and they have progressed considerably, particularly in recent times. Popular literature has developed from very modest beginnings, such as the old fairground ballad-sheets, to films, newspapers, journals, novels and comics. Popular art began with cave paintings, and has led to posters, shop window dressing, and pin-up photographs. Folk music began with tribal dances and country folk-songs, which have developed into jazz and dance music. Each of these modern popular arts is highly complicated, and requires great technical skill; but it exists to serve the same human needs as the primitive folk art from which it has developed. These needs have nothing in common with those which have given rise to true art. Some people seem to imagine that jazz is the characteristic music of our time, and that it can take the place of Bach and Beethoven. This is a complete fallacy. Jazz is only the characteristic *folk* music of our time, and its purpose is to give pleasure by appealing to the senses. In some ways it acts like a narcotic, such as tobacco, alcohol and drugs, for it provides a form of escapism from the duller aspects of our lives. The true modern successor to the Beethoven Symphony is the Symphony by Sibelius or Vaughan Williams, or some other modern serious composer.

I said earlier that the popular arts have progressed considerably. Progress implies improvement, or greater efficiency; and no one can deny that a modern thriller film, for instance, is much more efficient at satisfying man's craving for excitement than its early forerunner—the old ballad-sheet. The true arts, on the other hand, do not progress at all. They develop; they pass through phases and cycles; but they do not improve; in fact, very often the greatest achievements in any art are to be found quite early in its history.

Perhaps it is worth mentioning in passing that the divisions between the fine arts and popular arts are not always as crystal-clear as I have perhaps suggested: generalisations are always dangerous. You will find that it is possible to use a symphony orchestra and the techniques of "serious" music, yet write music in which rhythm is the most important factor. Such pieces really ought to belong to the same group as jazz, for they appeal to the senses. Ravel's *Bolero* and De Falla's *Ritual Fire Dance* are works of this kind. On the other side, it is possible to use a dance band and jazz conventions, and write a classic. The best example is Gershwin's *Porgy and*

153

Bess, which sounds like jazz but which nevertheless has
something very deep and revealing to say about the lives
of the negroes in the opera. It is therefore a classic.
Moreover, there is much borrowing between serious and
popular music. Dance music is always borrowing from the
classics; and, similarly, modern orchestral technique has
been greatly enriched, particularly as regards the wind
and percussion instruments, by discoveries made in jazz
bands. The same kind of thing applies equally in the other
arts. But on the whole my divisions will be found reliable,
and the criterion is always whether a work was written
on the one hand either for a useful purpose or to please
and charm; or whether it was written to stimulate serious
thought and uplift the spirit.

It is futile to argue, as people so often do, on the
relative merits of, for instance, jazz and serious music.
Since the two exist for fundamentally different reasons,
and satisfy utterly different needs, neither can ever super-
sede or supplant the other. It is ridiculous to condemn any
branch of applied or popular art; these arts are an essential part of our lives; we cannot do without them. On the
other hand, we must never try to substitute them for the
fine arts, for they can never lift us on to a higher plane
of human experience, or help make us more complete
human beings.

Now this is all very well, talking in vague general terms
about the importance of art in our intellectual development, but the fact remains that there are a good many
people to whom the fine arts are frankly a bore. Is it
possible, you may ask, to acquire a liking for such things?
Well, to a very large extent it is. In fact, there are very few
people who possess a good natural taste in all three of the
major arts. Most of us have a natural aptitude for one
or two, and have to develop a taste for the others. Many
people, again, do not really get to grips with the arts until
they are fully mature. But we should not excuse ourselves
on these grounds and neglect the arts completely, hoping
that we shall find them less of a bore in twenty years'
time. We ought to try to make some contact with great

art as early as possible, if we are ever to reap the full benefits later.

I propose therefore to devote the remainder of this chapter to a few "hints for beginners," which may be of use to those aspiring to find out what the arts have to offer them. These will have to be fairly elementary, and I hope that readers to whom they are already thoroughly familiar will excuse me.

I have already done a good deal of dividing up and parcelling into groups, but I'm afraid that one more classification is necessary. Classical music is divided roughly into two classes: programme music, which is either descriptive or actually tells a story; and absolute music, which usually describes not a scene or event, but a state of mind. Actually, the very greatest masterpieces are mostly absolute music, but programme music will provide a very good stepping-stone. In these days of radio and popular concerts there is no excuse for not hearing plenty of good music, and some of the talks on musical appreciation provided by the BBC are truly excellent. You will certainly know already some of the charming overtures, such as Mendelssohn's *Fingal's Cave* and *Midsummer Night's Dream*, and Weber's *Der Freischutz* and *Oberon*. Try to hear other works, such as Strauss's *Til Eulenspiegel*, Moussorgsky's *Pictures from an Exhibition*, and Rimsky-Korsakov's *Scheherezade*. But first make sure you are familiar with the stories behind these works. You will find them described in several books or, failing that, you are sure to find some musical person who can tell you about them. When you have become familiar with plenty of descriptive works of this kind, you might then begin to tackle a few symphonies, beginning perhaps with Dvorak or Tschaikowsky, and later Beethoven, Mozart and Brahms. It is essential that you should know a little about form before you start listening to symphonies or concertos seriously, although there is no need to go into the subject very deeply. Most symphonic works are in three or four movements, which are balanced both one against the other, and within themselves. The first movement is

155

usually built up out of two themes, which are played one after the other at the beginning of the work; then they are combined and developed at some length, and finally they are re-stated again at the end of the movement. The slow movement is often in a similar form, and is usually either sad or tragic. The third movement, if any, is usually either a rather stately minuet with a trio in the centre, in a symphony by an earlier composer, or else it may be a very gay lively scherzo, or "musical" joke, with a quieter centre section. The last movement is usually quite fast, and often is in rondo form. In a rondo, one principal tune is repeated several times over, with new material introduced between each repetition. When you get used to symphonic form, you will find that it has much in common with the composition in a great painting. The subjects which are balanced and combined so perfectly are like the shapes in a painting, and the orchestral tone resembles the colour balance.

You ought also to try branching out into Opera and Ballet. To begin with, try to see some of the comic operas, such as *Don Pasquale*, *The Bartered Bride*, and *The Barber of Seville*. Then you should try to hear a Mozart opera, such as *Don Giovanni* or *The Marriage of Figaro*. I can promise that you won't be bored by these works. Quite apart from the excellence of the music, they are extremely funny and will keep you interested and amused. At first you may even make the mistake of thinking that *Don Giovanni* is really too much of a lark to be taken very seriously, that it is about on the level of Gilbert and Sullivan and ought to be classed as light music. When you have heard it two or three times, however, you will come to realise that, underlying all the slapstick and comedy, the music has great profundity, and expresses much of deep significance about human nature.

As to Ballet, here also it would perhaps be best to start with some comic works, or "story" ballets. A few of the best are *Petrouchka*, *The Three-Cornered Hat*, *Façade*, *Job*, *Rake's Progress*, *Les Patineurs*, *La Fille mal Gardée* and *Pineapple Poll*. Later you ought to see *Swan Lake*,

156

Sleeping Beauty, Casse Noisette and *Coppelia*.

Now I must turn to Painting. Always remember when you look at a picture by a great artist that you are being allowed the wonderful privilege of looking at perhaps a quite ordinary scene through the penetrating eyes of a very great mind. An artist paints not so much what his eyes see, but what he feels about the objects or scene before him. That is why photography will never take the place of painting. Since the advent of photography, in fact, artists have begun to feel that there is no point in painting with realism, since if an accurate record of the appearance of a scene were wanted, the photographer would have been called in, not the artist. This has led to the modern extremes in abstract art, in which the painter paints quite frankly his feelings about a subject, and the mood evoked by it, without bothering to make his painting look much like the subject. Don't worry too much about abstract art. I am often amused in art galleries to see bemused spectators trying so hard to find some terribly subtle significance behind an abstract painting, when in fact the artist has merely painted a pattern in which the balance of shapes and colours arouses a particular emotion. There is no subtle significance in the painting at all! Don't be put off, either, by those Picasso paintings in which we are shown two views of a face in one picture. After all, if Picasso wants to paint two views of a face at once, why on earth shouldn't he? There is no reason whatever why he should restrict himself to the same limitations as the camera. When confronted by paintings of this kind, don't be worried by them because they don't resemble nature; just concentrate on the shapes and colours, and ask yourself: "What mood does this work tend to suggest: peace, tranquillity, strife, discord, anguish, fear, or something else?" If you can answer this question, you have understood the picture. Remember, also, that it is by no means necessary for a painting to be beautiful or even pleasant. Any type of emotion, any field of human activity may legitimately be made the subject of a work of art; and if a painter paints a picture intended

157

to make us recoil with a shock from the horrors of aerial warfare (like Picasso's *Guernica*), then we must not expect to see a picture which would look charming over the sideboard! As a matter of fact, this notion that ugly and unpleasing shapes and sounds can be used to describe violence in art has only really been carried to its logical conclusion in all of the arts in quite recent years; hence the discordance which is so often found in contemporary music. Freedom to use all kinds of artistic forms, however ugly, when wishing to express ugly ideas has existed in literature ever since the days of ancient Greek tragedy, and Shakespeare held nothing back in plays like *King Lear*. But it is only quite recently that composers like Stravinsky and Bartok have liberated music from the strange idea that it always ought to be pleasant to listen to; and Picasso and others have brought similar freedom to painting. Another factor which may be of help when studying modern works of art, particularly sculpture by people like Henry Moore, is that at the present moment artists and sculptors are very keen on drawing inspiration from very primitive works. This is an interesting illustration of what I said earlier about folk art influencing serious art, and it also illustrates how great art moves in cycles, so that earlier periods and styles frequently recur.

However, the most important thing about getting to like pictures is to acquire the habit of going to look at them, and going often. Remember that most of the picture galleries are free; that they contain works of fantastic value, which can immeasurably enrich our lives. There is nothing which so effectively opens one's own eyes to the beauties and potentialities of nature as looking at pictures. On a day of high winds, when great clouds billow across the sky, you will be reminded of the landscapes of Constable. Glorious sunsets, with brilliant colours streaming over the horizon, will remind you of Turner. When you have studied the impressionists, such as Pissarro and Renoir, you will one day quite suddenly see in the distance a great building, such as St. Paul's Cathedral, almost swimming in a soft ethereal haze of spring sunshine, and you will at once realise the truth that these painters discovered. Rembrandt will help you to see how much of a person's character can be seen in his face, particularly in contrasting light and shade. Go, then, to the Galleries. It doesn't matter much if to begin with you find yourself (according to those who think they know) liking the wrong pictures, or liking pictures for the wrong reasons. Your tastes will change as time goes on; that's half the fun of the thing. If at first you find yourself a bit bored by it all, then go round looking at old masters, trying to imagine from the paintings what life was like in the days which they depict; what travelling conditions were like; whether the people really look comfortable in such ridiculous clothes, and so on. You are bound to find some centre of interest, and from such small beginnings rich profit will one day be yours.

I must next say a very few words about Architecture. This, of course, is very much an applied art, and by modern standards a building tends to be considered beautiful only if it is also functional. Architecture is something which must greatly affect all our lives. We all have to live, learn and work in buildings, yet surprisingly enough probably fewer people take interest in the artistic qualities of buildings than in any of the other arts.

Where buildings are concerned, beauty is very definitely in the eye of the beholder, and often ninety-nine people will pass with blissful disregard a building which the hundredth finds interesting. Always when studying buildings bear in mind firstly their purpose, and secondly their context; or, in other words, whether they fit in with their surroundings. Notice how much more appealing a country village is when built of local materials. Always look out for buildings that have been carefully planned so as to get the best effect from the lie of the land. It is most important, also, to study the various styles of architecture, and although it is beyond the scope of this book to go into this subject to any degree, we have included a few sketches which may be of help to you. You will quickly realise what delightful results can be achieved when buildings over a large area are erected according to a plan, and with a consistent style. The squares of Bloomsbury and the Regency Terraces in Bath are admirable examples of this.

Finally, it is worth mentioning that although, as I have already said, buildings are pre-eminently "useful" objects,

ECCLESIASTICAL ARCHITECTURE

Norman   *Early English*   *Decorated*   *Renaissance*

DOMESTIC ARCHITECTURE

Elizabethan   *Georgian*   *Regency*   *Victorian*

THE THREE CLASSICAL ORDERS

Doris   *Ionic*   *Corinthian*

160

and are hardly ever built simply as works of art, yet it remains a fact that throughout all history—from the Temples of Luxor, the Parthenon and the Mausoleum, down to the new Coventry Cathedral of our own day— the buildings which move us most deeply by their beauty are nearly all cathedrals, temples or monuments; buildings which were designed for a purpose, but not for a purpose which is useful materially. The most wonderful buildings in the world were erected to the glory of God and man. This is certainly not a coincidence.

I would like to conclude this chapter by returning to the point at which I began. I believe that art is vitally necessary for the fulfilment of human destiny. It is not enough for mankind to go on living—

> "Living and partly living,
> Picking together the pieces,
> Gathering faggots at nightfall,
> Building a partial shelter,
> For sleeping and eating and drinking and
>   laughter"

—as T. S. Eliot so magnificently puts it, until the hand of death brings all things to an end. There is more in life than this. There is the divine self-expression of the human spirit. I believe that when men occasionally put into works of art flashes of genius, they are expressing the direct inspiration of the life-spirit itself: a momentary glimpse of God, an infinitesimal opening of the door, that for a brief moment we are at one with the very form of God; with Him Who gave us our life and being. If this is so, surely we are only truly alive in so far as we are able to capture these wonderful moments. They are not confined to the arts, but come to us also through natural beauty, and through religious experience; but the arts are full of such moments, and the study of art increases our receptiveness to such influences. The following passage from Bridges not only expresses my meaning admirably, but

F

161

is itself just such a flash of insight and genius:—

"Leave selfhood now in her fond sanctuary awhile
With the unseen universe communing, and entranced
Strangely:—As when a high moon thru' the rifted rack
Gleameth upon the random of the windswept night,
Or as a sunbeam softly, on early worshippers
At some rich shrine kneeling, stealeth thru' the Eastern
      Apse,
And on the clouded incense and the fresco'd walls,
Mantleth the hush of prayer with a vaster silence,
Laden, as 't'were with the unheard music of the spheres.
Nay, incommunicable and beyond compare
Are the rich influences of these moments of bliss,
Mocking imagination or pictured remembrance,
As a divine dream in the vaulted slumber of life.''

Chapter 17

FILMS AND THE THEATRE

DURING the First World War I used to go on a Saturday afternoon to the "penny rush" at the local cinema. One film I remember was *Shoulder Arms* featuring Charlie

"The 'penny rush'."

Chaplin. He lay down to sleep in a trench with a drain-pipe as pillow, and finding it too hard stuffed it with straw. But mostly it was "westerns," and if the manager had had a ha'porth of imagination he would have fitted saddles instead of seats, for we all joined in the inevitable chases. "'E's on 'is 'oss!" somebody would shout, and the pianist would thump out *Light Cavalry* while we all cheered the good 'uns and jeered the bad 'uns. The film may have been silent, but the cinema wasn't. Today we have Cinemascope, where you seem to be looking through a large letter-box, and Cinerama with the sound coming at you from all sides and the sensation of being swept into the action of the story itself—but in those early days I felt just as much part of what was going on. Integrity counts as much as technique when the director, cameramen, actors and actresses "on our imaginary forces work" to make us lose ourselves in their creation.

Every week eleven million seats are sold in British cinemas. You probably occupy one of them. How do you pick your films? I assume you do not go as a habit to the same place, same night, come hell or high-water. Do you follow the stars? They may be a guide, but John Mills and

163

Marlon Brando, to say nothing of Jean Simmons and Marilyn Monroe, do not always hit the jackpot, and every bright star began as a little twinkle somewhere—there are few meteors. It is fun spotting stars in the making. Perhaps you always go for a certain type of film—thriller, western, war, comedy, musical, romance? Why? If you once become interested in a film as a film, you greatly increase your field of enjoyment.

"I like a good plot," some of you say. Agreed. Most films fulfil our natural desire, as old as time, to be told a story. Life is a bit of a muddle, too, and to see the development of a series of events marching on to an inexorable conclusion, every word, gesture, incident, meaning something, gives us pleasure—like the solving of a quadratic equation. But documentary films can be enjoyable too—*Night Mail,* for example, and such photographic masterpieces as Sucksdorff's *The Great Adventure* and Disney's *The Living Desert,* where scorpions do a square-dance.

You may go to see a film because you have read the book (or the book-of-the-film-of-the-book-of-the-play!). Which excites you more? Have you ever wondered why they often alter the book? Shaw wrote a new ending for the film version of *Pygmalion* and Halas and Batchelor gave George Orwell's *Animal Farm* a happy ending in their cartoon version, of which most critics approved as being consistent with what the public expects of cartoon treatment. Read the book and see the film and make up your own mind about it. When a novel is filmed, on the grounds of word arithmetic alone, some telescoping is necessary. The parts of the story best for telling in terms of pictures are chosen. This may mean the writing up or down of certain characters and perhaps missing some out altogether. The wife in Cronin's *The Citadel* dies in the novel, but not in the film. Some directors think that the screen is more real than the printed page, and that the cinema audience does not like to see an unnecessary death, especially if it is a favourite actress. Fans object to her dying even on celluloid. Do you think the directors are right?

In a discussion on *The Colditz Story,* which is based on a true biography, a boy remarked that all the escapes and attempts to escape seemed fantastically unreal. Someone suggested it was because many months had to be compressed in less than two hours. Another quoted Aristotle's words that the probable impossible is preferable to the improbable possible—and if that sounds Greek to you, he meant that you can have a story you know to be untrue but the incidents hang together so well that they seem plausible, whereas a true rendering of accounts can be put across in such a way that you do not in fact believe them. A true story does not necessarily make a credible film or play. To Aristotle also is attributed the idea that a drama should observe the three unities of time, place and action; that is, it should last no longer than a day, keep in one place, and have no sub-plots. That would clip a cameraman's wings too much, but Carol Reed's magnificent *Odd Man Out,* the last hours of a gunman on the run in Belfast, observed them, and how many films are spoiled by an irrelevant love-interest? *The Caine Mutiny,* for example, which dealt with the reaction of different men in face of danger, had no need of a sub-plot of "silly slop."

I have mentioned some of the reasons why we go to the pictures—star or story appeal; for a laugh, a chill, a song, a spectacle; we have read the book. The psychologists tell us that we really go to escape from our ordinary humdrum existence. In the cinema itself we find bright lights, thick pile carpets, cushioned seats with a pretty usherette to show us to them, and when the lights dim we are anonymous and comfortably part of a crowd. Cecil Day Lewis, in his poem *Newsreel,* puts it like this:—

"Shown to your seat by a pretty usherette."

"Enter the dream-house, brothers and sisters, leaving
Your debts asleep, your history at the door:
This is the home for heroes, and this loving
Darkness a fur you can afford."

On the screen we live in expensive flats, have fast cars, we are beautiful women or tough men, the local boy who makes good, the secretary who marries her boss.

> ". . . you gape incurious
> At what your active hours have willed—
> Sleep-walking on that silver wall, the furious
> Sick shapes and pregnant fancies of your world."

Do you agree with the poet and the psychologist that people go to the pictures to escape for a few hours into a dream-world where they can compensate for all they lack in real life? If so, do you think it is a good thing? Herbert Hodge, a taxi-driver, once said that waiting on a rank outside a big cinema he noticed some people seemed to be in a dream and were shown into their taxis as if they were in the film!

There are several kinds of escape. The one that flatters us and sends us back home feeling that all the desirable things in life might drop into our lap one day, like the person in the pictures, does not help in the long run. The situation we are escaping from meets us again as soon as "God Save the Queen" is finished. But there is another kind that we experience when we see a film such as *The Stars Look Down,* which depicts the heroism of ordinary folk in the face of a pit disaster. We come away feeling proud and happy at the triumph of the human spirit. Even though some of the characters have died, we are not depressed. That is the hidden truth behind the old lady's remark, "I did enjoy it—I cried all the time." Death on the screen (or the stage) is a tragedy and not just a painful accident that nobody really likes to see, when it represents triumph, or the only honourable way out. If Romeo, Mark Antony, or Hamlet had not died, it would not have seemed a satisfactory ending.

A good film takes life and *does* something to it. It does not merely photograph it, hold a mirror up to it. It deepens it, shows us things that are there all the time but that we might otherwise not be aware of. It stimulates our thought and imagination—moves us, as we say. A work of art in any medium heightens our emotions and increases our understanding of life. A film does it by being "the flicks."

The essence of "filmness" is that it tells a story in pictures, not in words like a novel or play. It tells it to our eyes through pictures that move, and it is this whole feeling of movement that makes it so exciting. Compare the Stage and the Screen. In the theatre you sit in your seat and people are moving about in front of your eyes and you may want to see what is happening through the french windows on the stage but you cannot. The film camera, however, says, "Let's go and look at that face close to," or "This is what you must look at—this knife or this boot peeping from under the curtain, or this handle on the door." You may have dialogue or background music or sound effects as well, but the real excitement of the story comes from watching pictures move. The director can exploit movement in three ways: first there are the movements within the shot; second, he can move the audience by altering the position of his camera; third, there is the movement and rhythm of the cutting, the way in which one shot follows another. A simple illustration is the beginning of Chaplin's film, *The Pilgrim,* where in four shots the audience is put in possession of all the information it requires to get into the story.

> *Shot 1.* A poster with a face of a prisoner on it, easily recognisable as Charlie Chaplin. Underneath is some print. Camera closes up to the print, which reads: ESCAPE . . . BIG REWARD . . . etc.
>
> *Shot 2.* River bank with bullrushes. An unrecognisable man going in to swim away from camera.
>
> *Shot 3.* Man coming out and looking for his clothes.
>
> *Shot 4.* Charlie, dressed as a parson, walking on a station platform.

In less time than it takes to tell, the eye has picked up all that is necessary to go on with what is obviously to be an exciting and hilarious adventure.

In *The Belles of St. Trinian's* there is a mirthquaking sequence of quick-fire shots when the whisper goes round

the village, "They're back!" You do not see the girls
returning to school, but you do see shutters going up like
lightning on the shops, a policeman locking a door,
another fortifying himself with a nip of something, and
hens and chickens fluttering into their coops. The effect
is electric.

One of the greatest post-war films is *The Divided
Heart*, the story of a boy born of Jugoslavian parents,
who, after his village was occupied was adopted and
brought up by a German couple. After the war his blood
mother learns of his whereabouts and a United States
court in Munich has to make a judgment of Solomon.
The photography, acting and direction is worthy of the
theme. One sequence in particular stands out, showing
how camera movement can create suspense. The Jugoslav
mother looks out of her window, sees a man running and
hears a shot. The camera closes up to her hand gripping
the curtain she has drawn aside, and all that she is thinking and feeling is revealed in the clutching of her fingers.
We see the innocent faces of the children in bed. Like
her, we imagine it is her Partisan husband who has paid
the penalty of too much daring, and we share her relief
when we find we are wrong. Later on, we are shown a
German schoolmaster saying to a class of Jugoslavs,
"Adolf Hitler loves all children," and we hear another
shot. This time we have no doubt that the husband and
father, who was later captured, has been executed.

Although camera work is the basis of good filming,
sound—whether it is in narration, dialogue, music, or
effects—is an excellent handmaiden. Henry V soliloquises
in the English camp on the eve of Agincourt. His lips
do not move, but we hear his thoughts, which his facial
expression underlines. Incidentally, it is worth considering
the difference between acting for stage and for screen.
Celia Johnson says: "The nearer the camera gets to you,
the more accurate must be your thought—it's no good
looking as though you're just thinking; you must think as
the character must think." Bernard Miles puts it: "When
lovers gaze at each other from the closest possible range,

168

they can read the thoughts in one another's eyes, and pack a world of meaning into the flicker of an eyelid or the most delicate sigh. So it is in a close-up, except that the film camera and the microphone approach you with neither love nor longing, but with merciless curiosity and an insatiable hunger for truth."

Film music began in the studio when orchestras were engaged to play for the actors and actresses while they were being filmed. It was supposed to make them "tense for drammer." Then followed the piano in front of the silent screen vamping away to drown the noise of the machine operating the film. When projectors were quieter, the pianist could buy a book of scores with sections— "Hurry music for duels," "Storm scene," "Death scene," and so on. Opinions vary on the

"Piano in front of the silent screen."

use of music today. Some think it should be unobtrusive, others that it should be consciously listened to. What do you think its function in a film should be? The music that accompanies the credit titles often sets the mood for what follows. Did you enjoy the pot-and-pan tumpty-tum tune that heralded *The Belles of St. Trinian's*, or were you splitting your sides at the Searle cartoons? The zither playing in *The Third Man* and the hymn tune *Ein feste Burg* in *Martin Luther* each in their different way set the scene perfectly for the drama that followed. Addinsell, Benjamin, Bliss, Britten, Walton, Vaughan Williams have all felt it worth their while to compose special film music. Can you put pictures to their names?

I have not left much space to talk about the theatre, but much of what I have said about good cinema applies equally to good theatre. In both our thought and our imagination is appealed to, and we are caught up in the action. We know the actors are celluloid or, if flesh and blood, dressed up in wigs and costumes, and that we are

"We allow ourselves to be taken in."

not in Illyria but Waterloo Road, yet in spite of it we "suspend our disbelief," to use a phrase of Coleridge, we allow ourselves to be taken in—we just can't help it!

I think going to the play is much more an occasion than going to the pictures. There is no getting in half-way through the story and pushing in front of people in semi-darkness. Everyone starts at the beginning—or should do—and there is the excitement of buying a programme and seeing the curtain go up and sometimes smelling the scenery. You feel the actors are playing specially to you, which they are, and that waves of sympathy pass between you. How they perform depends partly on your response. This applies whether it is pantomime at the Palladium, Ibsen at the Old Vic, a miracle play in the ruins of St. Mary's Abbey in York, Shakespeare in a college garden at Oxford or outside the "George" in Southwark —anywhere "four boards and a passion" meet. Over coffee in the interval you discuss the show and then, at the end—well, here is how one young reviewer put it in a broadcast:—

"Have you ever sat in a theatre, spellbound, after the curtain has fallen on the last act, feeling that you couldn't clap because if you did it would be like clapping the sermon in church? After the last words have been spoken there is silence all around you as if everyone is holding their breath and then the house lights go up and suddenly they all come to life and begin to applaud, and only then do you realise that you have been watching a play and you want to clap louder than anyone."

She had been to see Shaw's *St. Joan* with Siobhan McKenna playing the part of the maid in Irish country-girl fashion, half fey and half feet firmly planted in a Galway bog. She believed in her and her voices and her last petulant cry, "O God, that madest this beautiful earth, when will it be ready to receive Thy saints? How long, O Lord, how long?"

Harold Hobson, the dramatic critic, says that "the mark of a good play is that it represents a profound experience, either emotional or intellectual, of a distinguished mind, expressed in theatrical terms." A *great* play is all that and "ecstasy" too.

"Adequate theatrical terms"—that is where production comes in. You should have seen *Macbeth* done by the Old Vic in their Edinburgh Festival production. The curtain rises and you expect to see the three witches, but instead a bloodstained warrior with agonising yell staggers across the stage. That strikes the note for as vigorous, full-blooded, pipe-skirling, roaring, ranting interpretation of the Scottish tragedy that you could ever wish to see. Acting, décor, costumes, music, effects, all combined to produce a play that you would hardly recognise as the one you did in the classroom with the desks pushed back and rulers for daggers. The stage dripped blood. Garrick once said to the murderer in the banquet scene, "There is blood upon thy face" with such power that the man replied, "Is there, by God!" At the Old Vic there was. As a young critic remarked, "We had soliloquies, yes, but they were exciting soliloquies made by men on the spur of the moment in a time of crisis. I came away feeling proud that the theatre could still show us something which in its essence is crude and savage but yet portrays the essential struggle of humanity against these things."

"*Have a go at acting yourself.*"

If you go to Silverstone for the racing, or to the Festival Hall for a symphony concert, you enjoy it all the more if you know something about how a racing car or a musical score is constructed. It is the same with going to see a film or a show. The more you know about direction and production, camera angles and acting, the use of music and effects, the more pleasurable and exciting the occasion becomes and, strange as it may seem, the illusion is not lost. Noticing the individual brush-strokes increases rather than your appreciation of the picture as a whole. There are books that will help you and film and dramatic societies and play-reading groups you can join. Be wary of critics, especially in the local Press, until by continual comparison of your judgment and theirs you find one you can trust. The best way, however, to learn what cinema and theatre really mean is to have a go at writing, acting, producing, filming, yourself.

Chapter 18

ACTING AND PLAY PRODUCING

B.-P. HAD a reason for most things; he had a good reason for being so fond of Amateur Theatricals. Dressing up; impersonating others; being "somebody else," all adds up to the plain fact that it can't be done without using your Observation! That's the reason B.-P. was so enthusiastic about Scouts tackling shows.

Unfortunately, far too many Scouts (and Scouters) today "put on shows" without the slightest thought to the observation of the characters they are going to play. An old wig is sufficient to make you an old lady; a hand on the hip makes you a silly girl. *No!* Such ideas only make you a stupid idiot. The same care you plan for your examination and swotting for badges toward the Queen's Scout goal *must* be used in the preparation for your next show.

Every movement in every sketch should be rehearsed and rehearsed, EXACTLY THE SAME, with each line spoken the SAME WAY and with the speaker standing in EXACTLY THE SAME POSITION, until perfection is

"Don't think an old wig is sufficient to make you an old lady."

reached. Every detail of tl e character should be studied long before the dress rehearsal so that you KNOW *exactly* how you will dress, stand, walk and speak; and once this is set at rehearsals, it is NEVER altered.

The operative word for all shows is REHEARSALS. It means work, and then more work. It is the only possible road towards a good performance, and there is no short-cut. It is the most serious of all things connected with the Drama or Revue, and the climax of the work you have

173

put in should be there before you at your Dress Rehearsal. Don't ever repeat that old-fashioned and never-true story of "a bad dress rehearsal means a good show." If you have a bad dress reharsal you should be ashamed of yourself. It is up to you to see (and want to see) exactly what you are going to give your public the following night. Every light cue should have been worked out and laid down on paper. *Nothing* is done unless it has been plotted and planned. Every performer comes on and goes off just as he has rehearsed, not one extra line or "piece of business" goes in on the first night that hasn't been rehearsed. Such is the conduct of the *true* performer. It is a ruling never broken by anyone who has the slightest intelligence.

* * * *

Before you commence rehearsing a play or a "Gang Show," blueprints must be drawn up of every item in the programme. The positions of each "prop"—where the chair is, the table, the door—all are marked on the plan and are placed on the floor during rehearsals so that each actor will know exactly where he is entering and what is in the room when he gets there. The distance between chairs and tables SHOULD BE MEASURED EACH TIME THEY ARE SET, until the property man has learnt the exact distance between each article. This is the beginning of the way to learn about that vital word, "detail." This is the beginning of the way to learn how to give the public a PRODUCTION.

Then for TEAM-WORK. The cast are like a football team: the more they play together, the more they understand each other. Each "move" in the show should be planned as you would plan an attack on a goal. Each knowing when to stand still to allow the other to "make ground," each "giving" to the other whilst he is progressing with the plot, whether it be in a short sketch or in a full-length play. Each one must know what the other is doing, and once "set" it must never be varied. A man cannot give a performance if he is not sure what the other one is going to do. No man is worthy to go on a stage UNLESS HE NOT

174

ONLY KNOWS WHAT HE IS GOING TO DO, BUT HAS REHEARSED, AND REHEARSED IT BEFOREHAND. It all adds up to the plain fact that putting on a show is a very serious business. Unless it is taken seriously, the result is usually something that should only have been put on in your own backyard, *not* in front of a paying public. You are a team who must learn to play together, and, in case I didn't mention it before, the only way you can reach this team standard is by *rehearsing*.

"Putting on a show is serious business."

We have a slogan with my boys in the London "Gang Show" which has gone through the years. This is it: "NOTHING KEEPS ME FROM REHEARSALS . . . NOT EVEN DEATH." Let me give you a few tips which form the background of our Gang rehearsals, because these may not be generally known, yet they are responsible for everything we have ever achieved. WE START AT SEVEN. WE

"Nothing keeps me from rehearsal, not even death."

START AT SEVEN—not five past, not one minute past. WE START AT *SEVEN*. To do that is the beginning of discipline. Every boy when he arrives comes over and shakes hands *before* he takes the floor. He never leaves at the end of rehearsals without again coming up to say goodnight. Why? Because I will not have any single boy sneak in or out of reharsals. I treat each rehearsal as I would my Troop Night. EVERY MOMENT IS PLANNED. I would never dream of going to a "Gang Show" rehearsal unless I had worked out beforehand what I was going to do each moment of the evening. This is bound to react on the boys. They know instinctively I have given it thought—that I know what I am doing—

175

and so I get their complete trust. That is every producer's job, and he can only win the trust of his cast by proving to them that he, too, has worked out each minute of the rehearsal time. Another little "line" we use right from the start: "If you get a part, you are lucky. If you *keep* it, you're luckier." Discipline is our keynote, but discipline with *fun*. The test of "fun" is what you achieve whilst you are having it. It just adds up to this: we make every rehearsal night an *event* for the boy. So must you in your rehearsals, even with the smallest Troop, for a rehearsal or a Troop Night must be an *event*.

Not only whilst on the stage is detail necessary. Many people who have been backstage during a "Gang Show" have been struck by the "order" of things, even with 150 running loose. We have no marshals—they are not needed because each and every boy knows exactly where to go, and WHERE TO KEEP OUT OF. Train your cast to "stand by" without always being called. They will get used to it and learn patience and loyalty to their pals who are on stage, keeping the curtain up and the show going until the "waiters" are due on. They will not stand *in* the wings but *back* from the wings. They must learn that the "prompt corner" is a no-man's-land where stands *only* the stage director.

*   *   *   *

MAKE-UP. It is not how *much* you use, it's how *little* you use that gets the best result. Few boys need cheek make-up, and only the *slightest* eye make-up. Never allow

some enthusiastic volunteer to plaster a face with everything he can lay his hands on. Red spots in the corner of the eyes are as useless as the person who puts them there. Dark lines above and below the eyes are about as much use on a boy's face as a mug of water in the ocean, except for the fact that it usually makes the poor lad look like the after-effects of a brawl. And don't— *don't—ever* put carmine or bright red lips

"Bright red on the lips of a Cub."

on a Cub or a youth who wants to look manly. (This particularly applies to older Scouters who have an idea that it may make them look younger—it doesn't; it makes them an exhibition!) There is an art in make-up, and the art lies in what is left *off,* not what you put *on.*

Finally, every time any member of your cast says, "It'll be all right on the night," give him a swift kick in the pants and don't let it be a light one. It will *not* be all right on the night unless you have made it all right at rehearsals. I started off by telling you how keen dear old B.-P. was on amateur theatricals. He gave us our Boy Scout motto, Be Prepared. Well, you must be prepared *before* you commence rehearsals for your show and then, through all the weeks of seeking perfection (and perfection is the only aim for a worthy member of our Movement) you must be prepared to study character, your lines, the direction given you by your producer, and the back-stage discipline that is part and parcel of every good performer.

Nothing must be left to chance. *Nothing.* Every detail must have been brought into play; the smallest "prop" used at every rehearsal, and then, on "the night," nothing will come strange. You will know (and will have used) the pen from the table, the book from the mantlepiece, the matches from the sideboard. Your performance will then be polished because you will be at ease; you will be at ease because you have rehearsed *properly.*

Let's get determined to raise up the quality of Scout shows everywhere. Let us be content with nothing but the highest standard, so let us learn how to go about it, the same way as we go about our next Badge. If these few tips and ideas help you, I'll be quite satisfied.

I wonder if I may add a personal note here. I have often been disgusted at the way various Producers (?) alter some of the scripts they get free of charge and which have been worked and found acceptable in the London Gang Show. Surely if you accept a script it is only fair that you abide by its contents and not alter it. Believe me, I write and RE-write these items time and time again

177

before they are ready for the London Show, so you mustn't blame me if I get annoyed when people with less experience decide they will do as they choose with these scripts. Let me tell you this story, as it may explain to you the outlook of some of these people. I went to a show a couple of years ago, where they also used two or three sketches for which they were *paying royalty*. In three cases they completely altered the wording (and in one case even the ending) of some of MY sketches. I asked the Producer afterwards if he ever altered the words of the scripts he hired, and his reply was, "Oh no, we can't change those because we are PAYING FOR THEM." Makes you fink, don't it?

Chapter 19

SOCIAL OCCASIONS

(1)

HAVE you ever noticed how some parties seem to go with a swing and to be such an easy success, while others, no matter how hard everybody tries, are dull and heavy and never seem to get going? I wonder whether you have ever asked yourself why this is, and if so whether you have arrived at the same conclusions as I.

Thinking back along the last fifteen years or so, I can recall a great number of parties in which I shared in some capacity or other and as is always the way with retrospection it is the pleasant ones that I remember. Of course, I cannot recall all the details of these parties, but there is

"... Outstanding or interesting guest ..."

a general aura of happiness around my reflections, and here and there something particular stands out; sometimes it is the food; something unusual or extra good I suppose; sometimes it is a game which was either original or which happened to appeal to me particularly just then; and sometimes it is an outstanding, entertaining or interesting guest who impressed me at the time and made a mark on my memory. But there is in contrast one other party which I do remember for its very awfulness—it was dull, flat, heavy, it never got going, nobody knew anybody, nothing had been thought out beforehand in the way of games, so that when a writing or drawing game was suggested, no paper or pencils could be found, and so on. Only the food was passable, and that was uninteresting but abundant. It may seem uncharitable to write in this way about hospitality

179

which I have received, particularly when I know that my host and hostess on that occasion were most worthy and well-meaning people; it was just that they had not got down to thinking about the party; it was to my mind, from the point of view of a guest, a typical example of an unsuccessful party.

So having thought back over these gatherings, which are of innumerable variety, I would say that the necessary ingredients for a successful party are:—

(a) The company, (b) the programme, (c) the food.

I think quite the most important factor in a party is the choosing of the guests. They should, of course, be people who like parties, and, if possible, especially in the case of a small party, they should know each other or at least have something in common. Personal friends from the Tennis and Rugger Club, for example, are better kept to their own party than mixed in with a gang of Scouts, who after all have their own peculiar jokes and interests.

A social is an ideal medium for combined Scout and Guide functions. A social does not really differ very much from a party except that it usually takes place in a hall rather

"Own peculiar jokes."

than in somebody's house, and is therefore a trifle less personal. It is also rather more highly organised than a party, which is necessary where people do not know each other well.

In either case, whether you have a social or party, it is necessary, if you want it to be a success, to have a programme worked out so that the thing runs smoothly and with none of those awful gaps when nobody has anything to say or knows what to do. A good party or social does need to be prepared with everything which is going to be needed, such as pencils and paper, at hand.

It is always a good plan to start off with the type of game which will mix people up and get them talking.

180

"Personalities" is a good old stand-by, and in case you have not met it, this is how it is played. You will need a good many slips of paper with the name of a prominent person on each. As the guests arrive they have a name (which they are not allowed to see) pinned on their back and they have to find out who they are by asking the other guests as many questions as they like. The answers

"Personalities."

may only be "yes" or "no," and when a player has guessed his name he is given another, and so on. It is rather old, but is so valuable as a "warmer-up" that I have no hesitation in mentioning it here.

Another good idea is to ask people to come portraying in some way that they are absent-minded: nothing so drastic, of course, as the man who turned up with only one side of his moustache, but something a trifle more subtle like shoes being laced differently or, for a girl, one earring missing. The object of the game is to discover everyone's "oddities" and make a list of same. No party could be very sticky after the scrutinising that has gone on during this game.

Yet another good "mixer" is to ask people to come wearing a picture to illustrate a film or a book title, a prize going to whoever guesses most.

Then there are all manner of competitions and the more original they are the better. Active ones are the best to have near the beginning before people have time to get rooted into a chair or fixed against a bit of wall where they seem likely to stay for the evening. Games with sides are a good idea, and even simple things go down well, like musical hats, which is like musical cushion, only instead you pass a hat which must be put on by each player and passed from head to head, so to speak. If you can find enough hats to give everybody one, except one player, the game is so hilarious that it usually ends by everybody just being crumpled up with laughter. We once

181

"Sack of assorted, well-chosen garments."

played another variation of this game which was passing a sack of assorted and well-chosen garments. When the music stopped whoever had the sack had to put in his hand, pull out the first thing that came, and put it on. I leave the rest to your imagination.

If you have the facilities, a Treasure Hunt is always popular, especially if played in pairs or groups; so is Sardines or Murder!

Or, of course, you could have a series of competitions with tables set out rather like a whist drive. At each table there is something different to do, such as getting dried peas into a bowl by sucking them up with a straw, or sticking pins into a bit of soap using only a pair of scissors to do it, and so on. You would want to have a time limit of about two minutes per table. The competition is progressive and must be arranged so that everybody does everything and against a different opponent. This needs a bit of working out, but is no trouble to anyone who is mathematically minded.

Another very good game, in fact one of the best, which never fails to cause endless fun, is the drawing game. For this you need to think out a list of subjects to be drawn and the more difficult the better, such as "The Man who Broke the Bank at Monte Carlo," "A Fog," "A Sponge," "How do you do?" etc., etc., and the poor unfortunate players who are divided into teams have to draw the things! One person from each team runs to the Games Master, and he tells them the first title on his list (the same for every team), then they rush to their corner, snatch their pencil and paper and proceed to draw. They may not speak one word, nor may they write anything, only draw and keep on drawing while the rest of their team are guessing like mad. Whoever guesses it right is given the pencil and he rushes up again to receive title

182

No. 2, and so on, until one team has exhausted the supply. It sounds almost impossible to draw some of the things I have suggested, but it is amazing how people, even those who cannot draw so much as a cat, will somehow make their team say the right thing. Well, I could go on suggesting games and competitions for a very long time, but I suggest you seek some for yourselves. You will find in your local public library under "Entertainments" several books on the subject. The main points to remember are: get people going; keep things alive; see that you cater for all guests by having a good mixture of games and competitions so that there is something for those not so bright; something for the quiet ones, and something for the noisy ones.

Now as to food. I think I shall say very little on this subject apart from mentioning a few general principles. See that you have more than enough for everybody. Make it look attractive. Get somebody else to do it for you!

Sandwiches are always popular and can have a good variety of fillings, e.g. sardine and salad dressing; cheese and apple; celery and sultanas; tomatoes; cucumbers; baked beans; lettuce; chicken; tongue; ham.

Open sandwiches look attractive, especially if cut into a variety of shapes and, of course, sausages on sticks are always popular and have the advantage of being filling, as do sausage rolls. Other ideas—mince pies out of season, individual hors d'œuvres, cakes, biscuits, trifle, fruit salad. In any case, you are sure to find some ladies who will be only too pleased to look after the refreshments for you: mothers love to help on these occasions.

There is one other way to deal with food and quite a good one. It is to ask each lady to bring with her a box containing supper for two. The boxes are then collected and the gentlemen, who should not know to whom they belong, either draw lots or buy them and share the supper with the lady to whom the box belongs!

(2)

We have talked so far about running parties and socials, which are on the whole informal affairs where most people know each other. Now with a Dance this is not the case. I am speaking of quite a big affair and not just a dozen people with somebody knocking out the latest jazz on the Troop piano which keeps on just as long as the pianist is willing to play. No, we will take it that you are thinking of running a bigger affair, perhaps, or should I say most likely, in order to raise Troop funds. Well, now, there are several things to remember:—

(a) The band, which may consist of three or more persons, according to your pocket and expected takings, must be booked well in advance.

(b) The hall must be booked well in advance.

(c) If you know somebody who will print the invitations or tickets for you, so much the better.

(d) An advertisement or two in the local shops or paper will help with your publicity.

(e) Some ladies of the Parents' Committee and other friends will no doubt deal with the refreshments for you.

(f) And last, but far from least, the M.C., and it is about the M.C. or master of ceremonies that I shall write further because his duties are numerous and so much of the success of the Dance depends on how he carries them out.

Now, what are his duties?

First, he should meet the band and discuss the evening's programme with them. They will want to know whether special numbers are required, such as "Elimination," "Excuse Me," "Spot," "Old Tyme" dances, etc.; whether you would like vocal numbers—this would probably require a "mike," and they may have a "speciality" of their own which should be enquired about. During the dance the M.C. will see that there is some refreshment for the band and will look after them generally.

Another of his functions is to announce the dances, and a word of warning here. The M.C. will need to be quite sure that he knows the sequence of the dances, especially the Old Tyme dances, because some of them require just a bit of organising to make them go with a swing. It makes all the difference to the Barn Dance, for instance, if everybody does it together and correctly so that the men all move forward at the right time. He must be prepared to explain any dances which need explaining, and to give a running commentary on how they should go. There is a very comprehensive book on the subject which is useful to have, *Old Tyme Dancers' Handbook*, by F. J. Mainey, which the County Library would obtain for you if it is not already in stock.

The M.C. can be invaluable, particularly at the beginning of the evening, by creating a happy atmosphere and getting the thing going. If people seem diffident about starting to dance, he should set the ball rolling by taking his partner (or anybody else's) and launching out as soon as the band starts up.

And now a word about Paul Jones. Some men are apt to slide out of this if they can, and so it is quite a good scheme to put them on the inside where they find it more difficult to do so. Another thing, and this is very important, the M.C. does not usually join in the circle, but stays around on the floor ready to dance with any lady he might see who has been left without a partner.

Perhaps you can think up a more original version of Paul Jones to make a change. The "Snowball" dance is a good one. One couple dances alone for a minute or two, the band stops playing, and each of the dancers chooses a partner from the onlookers; the four people dance, the music stops and they each choose another partner, and so on.

The M.C. will see that the right people are thanked at the end of the evening and will see to the tipping of the caretaker, etc. Those are the main functions of the M.C. He is really the host, or at least has all the duties of a host, so when deciding on your master of ceremonies, it is as well to bear that in mind.

(3)

While we are on the subject of social occasions, perhaps you would find a few tips useful about jaunts to town—

dinners, theatres, etc., and it would be a pity if your evenings were marred by feeling ill at ease through not knowing what to do, for while it is true that you can pick up a lot by watching other people and by experience, there must be a first time for everybody, and if you are sure of a few salient facts, you are that much better off to start with.

"Perhaps you are taking a girl-friend out."

Perhaps you are taking a girl-friend out; you want to impress her favourably? Well, look after her. Don't fuss, but be attentive. Walk on the outside of the path, open doors for her, let her pass in first, except in the case of alighting from vehicles, in which case the man should go first in order to turn round and give the girl a hand. Nothing looks worse than to see a man striding happily along on the inside of a woman, unencumbered by parcel or package, while she staggers as best she may on and off the kerb behind a load of parcels, unable to keep up without running a bit, and when at last their destination is reached and she dreams of a chair, he barges through the swing door leaving her to take the full brunt of it on the chest, parcels and all! She gets inside at last only to find she'll have to stand because he's already ensconced in the only chair. Do Scouts behave like that? I hope not!

If you are taking her to a theatre, buy her a programme; even if you are going halves in the tickets, buy her a programme and let her read it first. Help her on and off with her coat, and in a restaurant take her chair out for her if the waiter hasn't done it and let her sit down first. There is plenty of time, so don't hurry over it and nobody is staring at you, and if they are what does it matter? You are behaving as a gentleman should behave.

Having seated yourselves in a restaurant you will then

186

be presented with that complicated contrivance, a menu. If you are in luck it will be in English, but it is more likely to be in bogus French. If your knowledge of the language is not so good, don't try to talk—just ask firmly in English for what you want. If you can't read the menu at all, don't be afraid to ask the waiter what things are; he'll be quite used to it. Another way of geting over the difficulty is to ask him what he recommends and he will be delighted to suggest two or three dishes, which gives you a fair choice.

When dining out you may be rather puzzled at first by the seemingly complicated array of cutlery, but it is really very simple. You always use the implements from the outside first! Thus, you will find your soup spoon is on the extreme outside right, next comes the fish knife, then meat knife, etc. As you use them, or refuse a course, they are removed, so you cannot really make a mistake. The cheese knife is usually above the plate.

As for tipping, ten per cent of your bill is a good rule to go on for the waiter, but if you have drinks you should also tip the wine waiter and the cloakroom attendant, in fact anybody who does anything for you: that is why they are doing it and it is all a part of their wages. Expensive? Yes, but a pleasant change once in a while, although you should never plan an expedition such as this unless you could afford it. But there are special occasions in all our lives and then we should enjoy them sensibly and happily. A Scout is courteous—and well-behaved, and is therefore always at ease.

"The days that make us happy make us wise"—so will you allow me to wish you many happy days?

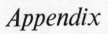

Appendix

Appendix

SIXTY SUGGESTED ACTIVITIES

1. Go on a rock-climbing or pot-holing expedition.
2. Spend a week sailing on the Broads.
3. Explore your county in a series of hikes.
4. Explore a river from source to mouth.
5. Find the "ghost roads" in your county.
6. Build kayaks or do a canoe trip.
7. Hike in the Pyrenees or somewhere else abroad.
8. Produce a play or concert or entertainment for a hospital.
9. Try a trek.
10. Write a film script and make a film.
11. Go on a night hike.
12. Have a "shadow scheme" arranged.
13. Go on a pilgrimage.
14. Exchange a weekend with Seniors from another County (or even District).
15. Visit factories or ports or newspaper offices in London (or Parliament or the Church Assembly), etc.
16. Go to a concert or the repertory theatre.
17. Arrange a gramophone evening.
18. Take up bell-ringing.
19. Take up sword-dancing.
20. Read up the ballet and then go to it.
21. The same with opera!
22. Do a course in Realistic First Aid (i.e. get in touch with Casualties Union).
23. Plan an attack on your Queen's Scout objective.
24. Have critical discussions on films, broadcasting, etc.
25. Have a weekend camp devoted to bird-watching.
26. Have a weekend camp devoted to fishing.
27. Have a weekend camp devoted to mapping.
28. Become a tree or wild flower or insect expert.
29. Organise a dance or social occasion.
30. Take up some branch of athletics: cross-country, javelin, discus, etc.
31. Improve your swimming.
32. Play tennis or badminton or squash or hockey or lacrosse or some other game.
33. Go skating or horse-riding.
34. Plan a course of reading: classical fiction or history or modern poetry, etc.
35. Get instruction in boxing or judo or unarmed combat.

36. Find opportunities for tree-felling or forestry.
37. Take up rope-spinning.
38. Have a hobby, e.g. keep bees or collect stamps, etc.
39. Attend a mountaineering camp or course.
40. Explore your home town (especially knowing its historical monuments, etc.).
41. Make some equipment for your Group or Church.
42. Make models (airplanes, etc.).
43. Become responsible for teaching all Tenderfoot Scouts in your Group to swim.
44. Become expert camp cooks.
45. Invent and try out new games for the Troop.
46. Make (and mend) toys for Group funds.
47. Make a tent or camp-fire blanket or duffel bags.
48. Survey a village and produce a log about it with photographs and maps.
49. Join a Library and use it.
50. Do a regular Patrol or Troop Good Turn to your community, district, church, etc.
51. Attend a Police Course.
52. Spend a week at Kandersteg.
53. Do some advanced knotting.
54. Practise abseiling, dead man's crawl, rescue work from burning house, etc.
55. Plan a winter camp.
56. Revise all the badges you wear (i.e. see that the contents of the bottle are what the label says!).
57. Camp at Gilwell.
58. Edit, contribute regularly to, or print the Group Magazine.
59. Take up falconry.
60. Link up with a Troop abroad.
61. The Silver and Gold Standards of the Duke of Edinburgh's Award Scheme.

The Prince
and the Pea

by Katie Dale and Ryan Wheatcroft

W
FRANKLIN WATTS
LONDON•SYDNEY

Chapter 1

Once upon a time there lived a lonely prince called Rupert. Every day, Rupert watched the village children playing. He longed to join in, but the Queen wouldn't let him. The village children were rough and tough. She was worried Rupert would get hurt.

"I know," the Queen thought. "Rupert needs a royal playmate! A nice princess to play games with." But how could she find the right princess?

The Queen read books to discover how other princes had found princesses. Some princes had rescued their princesses from tall towers, witches or dragons.

"Far too dangerous!" the Queen cried.

Another prince had held a ball, but ended up dancing with a servant girl in disguise!

"How awful!" the Queen gasped.

But how could you tell if someone was truly a princess? Suddenly, the Queen found the answer.

5

Chapter 2

"Rupert," the Queen cried, bursting through the door one morning. "Meet Princess Emilia!" Rupert's eyes lit up. He was finally allowed to have a playmate! He couldn't wait to play with Emilia.

But Emilia was no fun at all. All she wanted to do was play the violin – very loudly and very badly. Rupert covered his ears. He couldn't wait for Emilia to go home.

To Rupert's horror, the Queen invited Emilia to sleep over! She'd even made her a special bed, piled high with forty mattresses. Then, when Emilia went to brush her teeth, Rupert saw the Queen put a pea under the mattresses in Emilia's bed.

"What are you doing?" Rupert asked.

"I have a clever plan," the Queen smiled. "If Emilia can feel this pea through all these mattresses, it will prove that she is a **real** princess!"

"Why do you need to know that?" Rupert asked, frowning.

"Because only a real princess is good enough to be your regular playmate, my darling," the Queen said, hugging him. "Then you won't be lonely any more."

Rupert was worried. He'd rather be lonely than play with awful Emilia ever again! Then Rupert had a clever plan of his own. When the Queen wasn't looking, he removed the pea.

"Good morning, Emilia," said the Queen
the next morning. "Did you sleep well?"

"Very well," Emilia said. "That was the most
comfortable bed I've ever slept in!"

The Queen frowned. Rupert grinned. His plan
had worked.

Chapter 3

But the Queen didn't give up. She invited

more and more princesses to stay.

Each one was more boring than the last.

One girl spent all day gazing at the palace jewels.

One talked non-stop.

Another didn't

talk at all!

Every day the Queen placed a pea underneath
the towering mattresses. And every evening
Rupert removed it before bedtime.

I can't believe it," the Queen sighed. "None

of these girls are real princesses."

Rupert hid his grin.

"Oh well," the Queen said. "Princess Clarabel is

coming tonight. Maybe she'll be the one."

But the hours ticked by and there was no

sign of Princess Clarabel. A storm raged outside.

"Maybe she's not coming?" Rupert said, hopefully.

He'd had enough boring princesses to last a lifetime.

"Nonsense. She's probably just been delayed

by this horrible storm," the Queen replied,

gazing out of the window.

Finally, there was a knock at the door. A girl stood dripping on the doorstep.

"Hi," she said. "I'm — "

"Why, you must be Clarabel!" the Queen cried, hugging her. "We've been expecting you. Let's get you some dry clothes, and some dinner! What would you like? Smoked salmon? Roast venison?"

"Have you got any fish fingers?" Clarabel asked.

The Queen's eyes widened. "I didn't even know fish had fingers. How exotic!"

Rupert had never tried fish fingers before. They were delicious.

"Shall we listen to some music now?" the Queen suggested.

"I could play for you?" Clarabel offered.

"Yes please," the Queen cried. "How delightful!"

Rupert sighed. Not more horrible screechy violin music ...

But it wasn't. Clarabel played the drums.

"That was amazing!" Rupert cried. "Can you
teach me?"

"Not now, it's bedtime," the Queen said, quickly.

Chapter 4

Rupert couldn't sleep. Clarabel was the best

playmate yet, he hoped she'd be able to stay.

But what if she didn't feel the pea? It was very

small, after all. Maybe he should tell her about it?

He crept out of his bedroom on to the landing.

Then, suddenly, something hit his neck.

It was a pea!

"Ow!" Rupert cried.

"Someone put a pea in my bed," Clarabel said,

standing on the landing holding a pea-shooter.

"So I thought I'd return it."

Rupert felt his cheeks grow warm. "It wasn't me!"

Clarabel grinned. "Doesn't matter, I can't sleep anyway. Come on, I've found a much better use for all those mattresses."

Clarabel had heaped mattresses all round
her room.

"Whee!" she cried, jumping from one pile
to another. "They're like trampolines."

"What's a trampoline?" Rupert asked.

Clarabel just laughed. "Bet you can't jump
as high as me."

Rupert grinned and bounced after her.

It was great fun. He even tried somersaults!

Have you ever been sledging?" asked Clarabel.

Rupert shook his head. "Mother doesn't let me go outside if it snows. She's afraid I'll get hurt."

"Nonsense. Let's go now!" Clarabel cried.

"But it isn't snowing," Rupert frowned.

"Doesn't matter. We don't even have to go outside," Clarabel laughed. She grabbed a mattress and headed for the grand staircase.

23

"**Woo-hoo!**" Rupert cried, as they slid down the stairs on a mattress.

"This is the best night **ever**!"

"Yes it is," Clarabel grinned. "But now the sun's coming up. Back to bed! **QUICK!**"

Chapter 5

Just as Rupert and Clarabel had piled up

the mattresses again, the Queen walked in.

"Good morning," she said. "Did you sleep well?"

"Actually, I haven't slept at all," Clarabel

confessed.

"How wonderful!" the Queen exclaimed.

"You must come and play again,

Princess Clarabel."

"Hurray!" Rupert cheered, but Clarabel laughed.

"I'd love to come round to play with the Prince," Clarabel said. "But my name's not Princess Clarabel, it's Evelyn. I live in the village."

Rupert gasped. The Queen was astonished.

"Can Evelyn still visit, Mum?" Rupert asked, hopefully.

The Queen hesitated. But then she looked at Rupert's face. She'd never seen him so happy.

"Yes," she smiled.

"Hurray!" Rupert cheered and suddenly all the Queen's worries disappeared.

Her clever idea hadn't worked out as she'd planned. But, whether Evelyn was a princess or not, she made Rupert happy — and that was all that mattered.

Things to think about

1. Why won't the Queen allow Rupert to play outside with the other children?
2. How does Rupert feel when his mother invites the various Princesses to play with him?
3. What idea does the Queen have for finding a real princess playmate? Where did she get the idea from?
4. What are the similarities and differences with this story and the original fairy tale, *The Princess and the Pea*?

Write it yourself

One of the themes in this story is not following expectations. Now try to write your own story with a similar theme.

Plan your story before you begin to write it.

Start off with a story map:

• a beginning to introduce the characters and where and when your story is set (the setting);

• a problem that the main characters will need to fix in the story;

• an ending where the problems are resolved.

Get writing! Think about a fairy tale or traditional story you know and how you might write a new version of it to convey your idea.

Notes for parents and carers

Independent reading

The aim of independent reading is to read this book with ease. This series is designed to provide an opportunity for your child to read for pleasure and enjoyment. These notes are written for you to help your child make the most of this book.

About the book

In this twist on the classic fairy tale, the young prince is desperate to find a playmate. His mother, the Queen, only wants him to play with a suitable princess and devises a test to find one. But the prince and his mother soon find out that true friendship is more precious than being a real princess.

Before reading

Ask your child why they have selected this book. Look at the title and blurb together. What do they think it will be about? Do they think they will like it?

During reading

Encourage your child to read independently. If they get stuck on a longer word, remind them that they can find syllable chunks that can be sounded out from left to right. They can also read on in the sentence and think about what would make sense.

After reading

Support comprehension by talking about the story. What happened?
Then help your child think about the messages in the book that go beyond the story, using the questions on the page opposite. Give your child a chance to respond to the story, asking:
Did you enjoy the story and why? Who was your favourite character?
What was your favourite part? What did you expect to happen at the end?

Franklin Watts
First published in Great Britain in 2018
by The Watts Publishing Group

Copyright © The Watts Publishing Group 2018
All rights reserved.

Series Editors: Jackie Hamley and Melanie Palmer
Series Advisors: Dr Sue Bodman and Glen Franklin
Series Designer: Peter Scoulding

A CIP catalogue record for this book is
available from the British Library.

ISBN 978 1 4451 6338 3 (hbk)
ISBN 978 1 4451 6340 6 (pbk)
ISBN 978 1 4451 6339 0 (library ebook)

Printed in China

Franklin Watts
An imprint of
Hachette Children's Group
Part of The Watts Publishing Group
Carmelite House
50 Victoria Embankment
London EC4Y 0DZ

An Hachette UK Company
www.hachette.co.uk

www.franklinwatts.co.uk